ACHIEVE 100 PLUS

Reading

PRACTICE QUESTIONS

Laura Collinson

Acknowledgements

Rising Stars is grateful to the following schools who will be utilising Achieve to prepare their students for the National Tests: Chacewater Community Primary School, Cornwall; Coppice Primary School, Essex; Edgewood Primary School, Notts; Henwick Primary School, Eltham; Norwood Primary School, Southport; Sacred Heart Catholic Primary School, Manchester; Sunnyfields Primary School, Hendon; Tennyson Road Primary School, Luton.

Photo credits

iStock: p6 spider © CreativeNature_nl; p8 bottle © dimdimich; p10 bone © DWithers; p18 coins © ratmaner; p22 Osiris © HodagMedia; p24 stamp © traveler1116; p26 shoe © nicoolay; p28 puppy © jclegg; p30 phone © alexsl; p34 compass © harmpeti; p36 rubbish in sea © Big_Ryan; p40 helmet © andegro4ka; p42 gas mask © sumografika; p44 robin © GlobalP; p46 jelly and p48 blackberries © Valengilda; p50 mourners © A-Digit; p52 Pied Piper © nettel9; p54 envelope © DNY59

Text extracts

p6 Snow Spider by Jenny Nimmo. Text © 1986 Jenny Nimmo. Published by Egmont UK Ltd and used with permission; p8 Comfort Herself by Geraldine Kaye (© Geraldine Kaye, 1999). Reprinted by permission of A.M. Heath & Co Ltd; p10 The Turbulent Term of Tyke Tiler by Gene Kemp Published by Faber and Faber Ltd; pp12, 20 Pig Heart Boy by Malorie Blackman. Published by Doubleday Children's. Reprinted by permission of The Random House Group Limited; p14 The Serpent King in Seasons of Splendour by Maddhur Jaffrey. Published by Pavilion Books; p16 Arthur, High King of Britain by Michael Morpurgo. Published by Egmont; p18 Treasure Island by Robert Louis Stevenson; p22 315 words from First Puffin Picture Book of Stories from World Religions by Annabel Shilson-Thomas, illustrated by Barry Smith (Puffin Books, 1996). Text © Annabel Shilson-Thomas, 1996. Illustrations © Barry Smith, 1996; p24 The Anne Frank Exhibition © Anne Frank Trust UK; p26 The Curious History of Everyday Things by The Reader's Digest; p30 Children should be allowed to use mobiles in class © Daily Mail; p32 Approximately 270 words from The Commando Survival Manual by Hugh McManners (Dorling Kindersley, 1994) © Hugh McManners 1994; 34 Abundant Beauty: The Adventurous Travels of Marianne North by Marianne North. Reprinted with permission from Greystone Books Ltd; p36 Dumping Waste in the Sea © Daily Mail; p38 161 words from How Maths Works by Carol Vorderman (Dorling Kindersley 1996) © Dorling Kindersley Ltd, 1996; p40 Jousting: First published in AQUILA magazine 2013; p42 Autobiography by Adrian Henri, published by Jonathan Cape Ltd 1971; p46 The Magic of the Brain by Jenny Joseph from Sensational Poems; p48 Blackberry Picking from Opened Ground by Seamus Heaney. Published by Faber and Faber Ltd.; p50 Funeral Blues © 1940 by W. H. Auden, renewed. Reprinted by permission of Curtis Brown, Ltd; p54 Night Mail by W. H. Auden

Hachette UK's policy is to use papers that are natural, renewable and recyclable products and made from wood grown in sustainable forests. The logging and manufacturing processes are expected to conform to the environmental regulations of the country of origin.

ISBN: 978 1 78339 546 0

© Rising Stars UK Ltd 2015

First published in 2015 by Rising Stars UK Ltd, part of Hodder Education, an Hachette UK Company

Carmelite House

50 Victoria Embankment

London EC4Y 0DZ

Reprinted 2015

www.risingstars-uk.com

Author: Laura Collinson

Series Editor: Helen Lewis

Accessibility reviewer: Vivien Kilburn

Publishers: Kate Jamieson and Gillian Lindsey

Project Manager: Estelle Lloyd

Editorial: Sarah Davies, Rachel Evans, Anne Kilraine, Fiona Leonard

Additional questions by Maddy Barnes (p13, q6; p15, q6; p27, p6; p29, q5; p35, q1, 2; p45, q1)

Cover design: Burville-Riley Partnership

Illustrations by Dave Burroughs

Text design and typeset by the Pen and Ink Book Company Ltd

Printed by Craft Print Pte Limited, Singapore

A catalogue record for this title is available from the British Library.

Contents

Fiction

Non-fiction

Poetry

The answers can be found in a pull-out section in the middle of this book.

Welcome to Achieve Key Stage 2 Reading Practice Questions 100+

In this book you will find lots of practice and information to help you achieve the expected scaled score of 100+ in the Key Stage 2 Reading test.

It contains lots of reading extracts, some fiction, some non-fiction and some poetry. Each extract is followed by a selection of questions testing different reading skills, such as comprehension, making inferences, making predictions and the effect of language choices on meaning.

About the Key Stage 2 Reading National Test

The test will take place in the summer term in Year 6. It will be done in your school and will be marked by examiners – not by your teacher.

In the test you will be given a booklet containing a range of texts and another booklet for your answers. The texts will be from a range of fiction, non-fiction and poetry. The first text will be the easiest and the last text will be the most challenging. The texts and questions will be very similar to the texts that you have been reading in school.

You will have one hour to read the texts and complete the answer booklet. The test is worth a total of 50 marks.

- Some questions ask you to find the answer in the text. These questions are usually worth 1 mark. These make up 44–66% of the marks.
- Some questions ask you to write a short answer. These questions are usually worth 2 marks. They make up 20–40% of the marks.
- Other questions ask you to write a longer answer. These are worth 3 marks. They make up 6–24% of the marks.

Test techniques

Before the tests

- Try to revise little and often, rather than in long sessions.
- Choose a time of day when you are not tired or hungry.
- Choose somewhere quiet so you can focus.
- Revise with a friend. You can encourage and learn from each other.
- Read the 'Top tips' throughout this book to remind you of important points in answering test questions.
- KEEP READING all kinds of non-fiction, fiction and poetry texts.

During the tests

- READ THE QUESTION AND READ IT AGAIN.
- If you find a question difficult to answer, move on; you can always come back to it later.
- Always answer a multiple-choice question. If you really can't work out the answer, have a guess.
- Check to see how many marks a question is worth. Have you written enough to 'earn' those marks in your answer?
- Read the question again after you have answered it. Check you have done what the question asked you to do.
- If you have any time left at the end, go back to the questions you have missed. If you really do not know the answers, make guesses.

The snow spider

These questions will help you practise:
* explaining the meaning of words in context
* explaining how narrative content contributes to meaning
* identifying and explaining how language choices enhance meaning
* retrieving information
* identifying key details.

Gwyn waited until his grandmother had settled herself in the armchair and sipped her tea before he knelt beside her and took out the matchbox. He wanted her undivided attention for his revelation. Even so he was unprepared for the ecstatic gasp that accompanied Nain's first glimpse of the spider, when he gently withdrew the lid. The tiny creature crawled onto his hand, glowing in the dark room and Nain's eyes sparkled like a child's. 'How did it come?' Her whisper was harsh with excitement.

'In the snow,' Gwyn replied. 'I thought it was a snow-flake. It was the brooch, I think. I gave it to the wind, like you said, and this … came back!'

'So,' Nain murmured triumphantly, 'you are a magician then, Gwydion Gwyn, as I thought. See what you have made!'

'But did I make it, Nain? I believe it has come from somewhere else. Some far, far place … I don't know, beyond the world, I think.'

'Then you called it, you brought it here, Gwydion Gwyn. Did you call?'

'I did but …' Gwyn hesitated, 'I called into the snow, the names you said: Math, Lord of Gwynedd, Gwydion and Gilfaethwy. Those were the only words.'

'They were the right words, boy. You called to your ancestors. The magicians heard your voice and took the brooch to where it had to go, and now you have the spider!' Nain took the spider from Gwyn and placed it on her arm. Then she got up and began to dance through the shadowy wilderness of her room. The tiny glowing creature moved slowly up her purple sleeve, until it came to her shoulder, and there it rested, shining like a star beneath her wild black curls.

Gwyn watched and felt that it was Nain who was the magician and he the enchanted one.

Suddenly his grandmother swooped back and, taking the spider from her hair, put it gently into his hands. 'Arianwen,' she said. 'White silver! Call her Arianwen; she must have a name!'

'And what now?' asked Gwyn. 'What becomes of Arianwen? Should I tell about her? Take her to a museum?'

'Never! Never! Never!' said Nain fiercely. 'They wouldn't understand. She has come from another world to bring you closer to the thing you want.'

'I want to see my sister,' said Gwyn. 'I want things the way they were before she went.'

Nain looked at Gwyn through half-closed eyes. 'It's just the beginning, Gwydion Gwyn, you'll see. You'll be alone, mind. You cannot tell. A magician can have his heart's desire if he truly wishes it, but he will always be alone.'

Jenny Nimmo

1 *He wanted her undivided attention for his revelation.*

Explain what the phrase *undivided attention* means.

_____

_____

1
(1 mark)

2 Look at the first paragraph.

What does the phrase *Nain's eyes sparkled like a child's* tell you about how Nain was feeling?

_____

_____

2
(2 marks)

3 Explain why the writer has used an ellipsis in the phrase *and this … came back!*

_____

_____

3
(1 mark)

4 **Find** and **copy** the words or phrase which tells you that Gwyn didn't believe that he could do magic.

_____

4
(1 mark)

5 **Find** and **copy** an example of a simile in the text.

_____

_____

5
(1 mark)

6 What is the effect of repeating the words *Never! Never! Never!*?

_____

_____

6
(1 mark)

7 Nain wasn't afraid of the spider.

Give **two** details from the text to support this.

1. _____

2. _____

7
(2 marks)

/ 9

Total for
this text   7

Comfort at the market

These questions will help you practise:
★ explaining the meaning of words in context
★ explaining how language choices enhance meaning
★ retrieving and recording information
★ making inferences
★ explaining inferences.

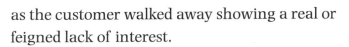

Comfort settled on a wooden box behind the stall and gazed across Akwapawa market. At last she had got herself to the market there where she wanted to be, just as she had got herself into Ghana. The shrill tumult rang in her ears. There was a concrete floor and, high above her head, a corrugated iron roof supported on green painted pillars mottled with rust. There were dozens of stalls under the roof and outside its protection there were women sitting with baskets as far as the eye could see. Hundreds of women who simply laid their goods out on the ground: oranges, yams, cassava, tomatoes and lettuces grown on their own farms; cloth, soap and plastic combs bought to trade.

Everything was round: round woven baskets like cottage loaves, round head-scarves circled the heads of married women, round fruit in round piles, round bumps of babies tied to their mothers' backs. The market women themselves were round too as they settled like plump pears on the ground beside their goods, *bottom power* as it was called, the power of the market mammies. Even the patterns on their cloths were round, Ata's had round yellow leaves on a black ground, Abla's at the next stall had scarlet vines with round dark-blue fruits, balloons floated on Comfort's.

The hubbub bounced against the roof and echoed back, morning greetings, babies crying, lorries revving, the shout of book-men and the cries of the market women calling to possible customers, their voices falling with a lower price as the customer walked away showing a real or feigned lack of interest.

'And who is this then?' Abla shouted above the din and her smile flashed white. She had a baby sleeping on her back and two small children playing on the ground beside her.

'Comfort, child of my brother, Mante,' Ata said but her eyes were anxious as she settled Bolo on a bed of cloth under the stall. Bolo was feverish. The fetish priest had given medicine but the child seemed no better.

'Ah, Comfort who comes from England,' Abla said. 'No wonder she stares like an owl caught in the daylight. The stranger has big eyes but does not see what is happening.' Comfort smiled gently to herself. She was surely no stranger who was allowed to come to Akwapawa market to watch her Grandmother's lorry as well as learn to trade in cloth.

'I have brought the medicine,' Abla said, handing a bottle of spinach-green liquid to Ata. 'My son, Dublo, had a fever and bad leg just the same as Bolo and now he is well, Onyame be praised. Dublo, hold out your leg.' There was a grey scar patch where the sore had healed. Many of the children round the market had such grey scars.

'How much do I owe you?' Ata said, pouring a large dose into a cup for Bolo.

'Pay me when the child is well,' Abla said with a shrug.

Comfort Herself by Geraldine Kaye

1 *The shrill tumult rang in her ears.*

Explain why the word *tumult* is an effective way to describe the sound in the market.

_____

_____

2 Read the paragraph beginning: *The hubbub bounced....*

Explain the sights and sounds described.
Refer fully to the text in your answer.

_____

_____

_____

_____

_____

3 What is the relationship between Ata and Comfort?

_____

4 Why was Ata anxious about Bolo?

_____

5 *No wonder she stares like an owl caught in the daylight.*

Why has the writer used the **simile** *she stares like an owl caught in the daylight* to describe Comfort?

_____

_____

6 Explain how the writer shows that this is a story from another culture.

Give **two** examples from the text.

1. _____

2. _____

The mysterious bones

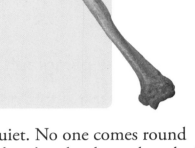

These questions will help you practise:
★ summarising main ideas
★ explaining how narrative content contributes to meaning
★ identifying key details
★ giving the meaning of words in context
★ making and explaining inferences
★ making predictions
★ making comparisons.

'*Dem bones, dem bones gonna roll around…*'

'*What's the fastest thing in the water?*'

'*A motor pike.*'

'You've got bones on the brain. That's because you're a bonehead I suppose …'

'But I tell you it's a real skellinton, Tyke. I tell you where I seen it. Down in the **leat**. I went there yesterday when you was out. Come on. Come and look. I bet it's somebody what's bin murdered.'

'I got into enough trouble over that marrow bone …' But Danny had set off along the road as if he was warming up for the fifteen hundred metres. He belted down the bank, where the old city walls stand, that drops down to the river and the leats, the oldest part of the city, Sir says. I soon caught up with him, Crumble at my heels, her ears ruffling out in the wind.

'Which leat are the bones in?'

There are two, Cricklepit and Walter, that cut off from the river below the weir. The leats and the river make an island that's mostly a deserted place. Danny panted:

'By the bridge. Near the warehouses.'

'They weren't there last week.'

'The rain and high water brung 'em out.'

We ran on, past the old, broken water-wheel, hidden in the trees and bushes, where the kingfisher flies sometimes. I've seen him quite a lot lately. I threw a broken brick into the water **sluicing** through an iron grid. The brown colour had gone but it was still high.

Everywhere was quiet. No one comes round here much. Everything's either being knocked down or rotting away; it's a place for secrets and adventures.

Perhaps this was an adventure. Perhaps the bones were the skeleton of a murdered man, or valuable prehistoric remains. We ran through the square where my Gran used to live before it was demolished and on to a little sandstone bridge. Beside it was a wall and a railing and a long drop to the leat. We climbed over and inspected the filthy water.

'There. There it is.'

Danny pointed at what looked like a huge set of teeth decorated with floating strands of green slime. Other bones were scattered around. Crumble made eeking noises on the other side of the wall, so I lifted her over.

'It's lovely, Tyke.'

'It's a sheep, you nutter. It's like that one Martin Kneeshaw brought off the moor and went round showing off.'

'No it's not. It's a man, I tell you. Somebody murdered that man and chucked his body in here and he mouldered and mouldered away till he was that skellinton.'

'It's a sheep …'

He took no notice.

The Turbulent Term of Tyke Tiler by Gene Kemp

Glossary

- **leat** a ditch supplying water to a watermill
- **sluicing** flowing

1 Write **one** sentence to explain what Tyke and Danny are doing in this story.

_____

_____

(1 mark)

2 Why are the first three lines written in **italics**?

_____

_____

2
(1 mark)

3 In the story, Tyke doesn't believe Danny.
Give **two** key details to support this.

1. _____

2. _____

3
(2 marks)

4 The writer has used language from the region in which the story is set.

Write the Standard English word or phrase next to each regional word or phrase.
The first one has been done for you.

4
(1 mark)

Regional word or phrase	Standard English word or phrase
you was out	_you were out_
skellinton	
what's bin murdered	
brung	

5 Who is the **narrator** of the story?
Give **one** example to support your answer.

_____

_____

_____

5
(1 mark)

6 What might Tyke do with the skeleton and how might this be different from what Danny might do?

_____

_____

_____

6
(2 marks)

/ 8

Total for this text

11

Underwater peace

These questions will help you practise:
★ explaining how narrative content contributes to meaning
★ explaining how language choices enhance meaning
★ making comparisons
★ identifying key details
★ explaining inferences
★ summarising main ideas.

The noise was deafening. Shouting, screaming, laughing, shrieking – it was so thunderous. I thought my head was about to explode. I took a deep breath, breathed out, inhaled again, then dipped down until my head was completely underwater.

Silence.

Peace.

It was like a radio being switched off. I sat down at the bottom of the swimming pool and opened my eyes. The chlorine in the water stung, but better that than not seeing what was coming and being kicked in the face. I would've liked to stay down there for ever, but within seconds my lungs were aching and there came a sharp, stabbing pain in my chest. My blood roared like some kind of angry monster in my ears.

I closed my eyes and stood up slowly. If I had to emerge, it would be at my own pace and in my own time – no matter how much my body screamed at me to take a breath as fast as I could. I was the one in control. Not my lungs. Not my blood. Not my heart.

'Cam, are you all right?'

I opened my eyes. Marlon stood in front of me, his green eyes dark and huge with concern. I inhaled sharply, waiting for the roaring in my ears to subside. The pain in my chest took a little longer. 'Course! I'm fine,' I replied a little breathlessly.

'What were you doing?'

'Just sitting down.'

Marlon frowned. 'Is that smart?'

'I was just sitting down. Don't fuss. Sometimes you're worse than Mum and Dad,' I said.

'If your parents find out that you're here every Tuesday instead of at my house, I'm the one who'll get it in the neck – and every other bodily part,' Marlon pointed out.

I smiled. 'If you don't tell them, I won't.'

'How can you be so calm about it? Every time we come here, I'm terrified some grownup who knows your family is going to spot you and tell your parents.' Marlon looked around the pool anxiously, as if expecting his words to come true at that precise moment.

'Marlon, you worry too much.' My smile broadened as the pain in my chest lessened.

'How long were you underwater?'

'A few seconds. Why?'

'I really don't think you should ...'

I'd had enough. 'Marlon, bog off!' I snapped. 'You're getting on my last nerve now!'

'I was just ...'

'I know what you were doing, and you can stop it,' I said firmly. 'You're beginning to cheese me off.'

Marlon clamped his lips together tight and looked away. He was hurt and we both knew it. I fought down the urge to apologise. Why should I say I was sorry? Marlon knew how much I hated to be clucked over. But, as always, I caved in.

Pig Heart Boy by Malorie Blackman

1 Look at lines 7 and 8. Explain why the writer has written the words *Silence* and *Peace* on two separate lines.

_____

(1 mark)

2 *My blood roared like some kind of angry monster in my ears.*

Explain the effect of comparing the blood to an *angry monster*.

_____

_____

(1 mark)

3 Explain how Cam's character is different to Marlon's character.

_____
_____
_____
_____

(3 marks)

4 Marlon is a good friend to Cam.
Give **two** details that support this idea.

1. _____

2. _____

(2 marks)

5 What can you infer about Cam's health?
Explain fully, referring to the text in your answer.

_____
_____
_____
_____
_____

(3 marks)

6 Using information from the text, tick one box in each row to show whether each statement is **true** or **false**.

	True	False
There was chlorine in the water.		
Marlon had brown eyes.		
Cam was under the water for a minute.		

(1 mark)

/11

Total for
this text

13

Krishna fights the Serpent King

These questions will help you practise:
★ explaining the meaning of words in context
★ explaining how narrative content contributes to meaning
★ identifying and explaining how language choices enhance meaning
★ identifying key details from fiction
★ making predictions
★ explaining inferences.

Kaliya, the Serpent King, was no ordinary snake. He had five heads and was so large that he could crush humans to death in a matter of seconds. The Serpent King lived under the darker whirlpools of the Yamuna River and this is where he held his court. Whenever he so wished, he would rise out of the water and lay waste the countryside, ferociously breathing fire and black smoke wherever he went.

Krishna was almost twelve years old by now. Even at this tender age, he was the acknowledged leader among his friends and looked upon with great respect by the large community of nomadic cowherds that moved wherever the pasture was good.

One day, a group of cowherds came to Krishna and said, 'Kaliya must be stopped. He has already swallowed 300 chickens, 178 goats, and 83 cows. Yesterday he killed the blacksmith's son. This is the last straw. Anyone that tries to cross the river, swim, graze cattle, grow watermelons, milk goats or even walk by the river is in danger. Something must be done.'

Krishna collected a group of brave friends and walked towards the edge of the water. Suddenly, a cloud of black smoke rose above the river. Shooting flames swirled upwards and, in one quick swipe, Kaliya encircled all of Krishna's friends in the curl of his body and dragged them down to the bottom of the river.

Having done their dirty deed, the five dreaded heads bobbed up again, breaking the surface of the water. This time the Serpent King was floating along casually, mockingly.

Krishna took one flying leap and landed on all the five hooded heads of the dreaded snake. He crushed one head under one arm and another head under another arm. With his feet he began a heavy-footed dance on the remaining three.

Kaliya felt as if all the mountains of the Himalayas were raining on his head. Such was the power of Krishna's feet.

He decided to dive into his underwater court. He would drown Krishna this way.

Seasons of Splendour by Madhur Jaffrey

1 Look at the first paragraph. Explain what the phrase *he held his court* means.

_____

(1 mark) 1

2 Look at the third paragraph. Explain the effect of describing the numbers of animals the serpent had killed.

_____

_____

(1 mark) 2

3 *Kaliya felt as if all the mountains of the Himalayas were raining on his head.*

a) This sentence is an example of…

Tick **one**.

a simile. ☐

personification. ☐

a metaphor. ☐

onomatopoeia. ☐

(1 mark) 3a

b) What does the sentence tell you about how Kaliya is feeling?

_____

(1 mark) 3b

4 Number the events from **1** to **5** in the order in which they happen in the story.

Krishna landed on the heads of the serpent. ☐

Krishna's friends were drowned. ☐

Kaliya killed the blacksmith's son. ☐

The serpent burnt the countryside. ☐

Kaliya returned to his court. ☐

(1 mark) 4

5 Explain what might happen next in the story.

_____

_____

(1 mark) 5

6 How can you tell Krishna's powers were stronger than Kaliya's?

_____

_____

_____

(1 mark) 6

/7

Total for this text

15

Dangerous visitors

These questions will help you practise:
* ★ explaining inferences
* ★ giving the meaning of words in context
* ★ retrieving information and identifying key details
* ★ explaining the meaning of words in context
* ★ summarising main ideas.

The next morning I was up early. I met Merlin on the ramparts. He was looking out over the mist-covered marshes. There were three horses plodding slowly along the causeway, legless in the mist. 'Look,' said Merlin sadly. 'They have come. I feared they might.'

'Who are they?' I asked. As they came closer, I noticed that one of them had a child riding in front of her.

'Those are your three half-sisters, Arthur, your mother Igraine's daughters by Gorlois, children of her first marriage. I have told you about them before. Elaine and Margawse have come to make their peace with you, I have no doubt. But do not trust them. Remember, neither Elaine nor Margawse have any great cause to love you. Your half-sisters they may be but both are widowed, and by you too. Pelinore might have killed their husbands, King Nantes and King Lot, but it was in your name that he fought them. Take care. Take care.'

'So the third must be Morgana Le Fey,' I said, 'the youngest.'

Merlin's eyes narrowed and a shiver came over him so that he had to lean against the ramparts to steady himself. 'I hoped never to see her here in Camelot,' he said. 'Of all the people on this earth, she is the one who most threatens you. She may look like an angel, but she has the soul of the very devil, and all his evil powers too, powers that I can no longer stand against. In my youth I might have done, but not now, for my own powers are waning. Sometimes I think they are almost gone. Beware of her, Arthur, beware of her, I tell you. She would have your kingdom for herself and, if she cannot have it, then she will do all she can to destroy it, and you with it.'

'Who is the child?' I asked, but Merlin did not seem to want to answer. I asked again.

'You do not want to know,' Merlin replied, and he looked away quickly. 'Not on your wedding day. I will cast no dark shadows on such a day.'

As I looked at the three riders I was filled with a terrible sense of foreboding. 'You promised me once, Merlin,' I said, steeling myself, 'that you would never tell me the future unless I asked you to, nor deny me the truth if ever I asked it. I have never asked what shall become of me, or of my kingdom – although I know you could tell me. I do not want to know, for if I once know the end of it all and how I will get there, then there would be little reason to live my life through. If that child is part of my future, then tell me. Tell me at least who he is.'

Arthur, High King of Britain by Michael Morpurgo

1 Explain how you know that Merlin was expecting the visitors.

_____

_____

1 (1 mark)

2 *... neither Elaine nor Margawse have any great cause to love you.*

What does the word *cause* mean in this sentence?

_____

2 (1 mark)

3 Merlin advises Arthur not to trust Elaine and Margawse.

Explain why they are not to be trusted.

_____

_____

_____

_____

_____

3 (3 marks)

4 **Find** and **copy** a phrase or sentence that tells you that Merlin is uncomfortable with the arrival of Morgana Le Fey.

_____

4 (1 mark)

5 Explain why the word *waning* has been used to describe Merlin's powers.

_____

5 (1 mark)

6 In the last paragraph, beginning *As I looked at the three riders...*, Arthur is *filled with a terrible sense of foreboding.*

Write **one** sentence that summarises his thoughts.

_____

6 (1 mark)

/8

Total for this text

17

Treasure Island

These questions will help you practise:
★ summarising main ideas
★ identifying and explaining how language choices enhance meaning
★ making inferences
★ identifying the sequence of events
★ explaining how narrative content contributes to meaning
★ explaining inferences.

The next morning we fell early to work, for the transportation of this great mass of gold near a mile by land to the beach, and thence three miles by boat to the *Hispaniola*, was a considerable task for so small a number of workmen. The three fellows still **abroad** upon the island did not greatly trouble us; a single sentry on the shoulder of the hill was sufficient to insure us against any sudden onslaught, and we thought, besides, they had had more than enough of fighting.

Therefore the work was pushed on briskly. Gray and Ben Gunn came and went with the boat, while the rest, during their absences, piled treasure on the beach. Two of the bars, slung in a rope's-end, made a good load for a grown man – one that he was glad to walk slowly with. For my part, as I was not much use at carrying, I was kept busy all day in the cave, packing the minted money into bread-bags.

It was a strange collection, like Billy Bones's hoard for the diversity of **coinage**, but so much larger and so much more varied that I think I never had more pleasure than in sorting them. English, French, Spanish, Portuguese, **Georges** and **Louises**, doubloons and double guineas and **moidores** and sequins, the pictures of all the kings of Europe for the last hundred years, strange Oriental pieces stamped with what looked like wisps of string or bits of spider's web, round pieces and square pieces, and pieces bored through the middle, as if to wear them round your neck – nearly every variety of money in the world must, I think, have found a place in that collection; and for number, I am sure they were like autumn leaves, so that my back ached with stooping and my fingers with sorting them out.

Robert Louis Stevenson

Glossary

- **abroad** on the run
- **coinage** coins
- **Georges** gold coins with the head of King George
- **Louises** gold coins with the head of King Louis
- **moidores** 18th-century Portuguese gold coins

1 Write a suitable heading for the first two paragraphs of the text.

_____

☐ 1
(1 mark)

2 a) Towards the end of the text what does the writer compare the coins to?

_____

☐ 2a
(1 mark)

b) How is this an effective way to describe the coins?

_____

_____

☐ 2b
(2 marks)

3 Number the events involved in moving the gold **1** to **5** in the order in which they happen in the story.

Treasure was put into piles. ☐

The coins were sorted out. ☐

Two men sailed the boat to the ship and back. ☐

The coins were put into bread-bags. ☐

A soldier kept watch on the hill. ☐

☐ 3
(1 mark)

4 Explain in **one** sentence what the description of the coins tells you about the origin of the coins.

_____

☐ 4
(1 mark)

5 Was moving the gold an easy task?

Explain fully, referring to the text in your answer.

_____
_____
_____
_____
_____

☐ 5
(3 marks)

/ 9

Total for this text

19

Cameron faces the press

These questions will help you practise:
- ★ explaining how narrative content contributes to meaning
- ★ explaining how language choices enhance meaning
- ★ explaining inferences
- ★ explaining the meaning of words in context
- ★ making inferences
- ★ making comparisons.

I could still hear them screaming at me.

'CAMERON, HOW D'YOU FEEL …?'

'CAMERON, WHAT'S IT LIKE TO HAVE A PIG HEART …?'

'WHY DID YOU DO IT …?'

'HOW LONG WILL YOU LIVE NOW …?'

'CAMERON …?'

'CAMERON …?'

On and on it went, on and on and on like a relentless tide. The police shifted to make a ring directly around us, excluding the car. And still the shouting and screaming and yelling and calling continued. There were TV cameras and camcorders all around. The police edged towards our house with us in the middle. When I'd seen movie stars or pop stars surrounded by their bodyguards and their fans on the telly before, I'd always thought that it must be fun to be famous. But if this was what it was like, then it was more terrifying than anything else. I looked around at the expressions on the faces of those immediately around us, beyond the police ring. They scrutinized me with rapt attention. Some of them were staring at me as if I'd just sprouted another head or something.

We moved up our garden path, through the heaving crowds, with the police and Dad yelling something about trespassing. And for the first time since my operation, I could hear my blood roaring in my ears. The roar was so loud it began to drown out the noise around me. Everyone and everything started to get swimmy and blurry.

I was going to faint.

No! NO! Not in front of these people, I told myself frantically. What would Mum and Dad say? What would my friends say? I'd never live it down. I took a deep breath, then another and another. We were close to the front door now. Dad struggled to get the front door key in the lock. Intense lights blinked on and off all around us like mini lightning bolts. I turned my head slightly and was immediately blinded by more camera flashes. The front door opened.

Come on, Cameron. Breathe in. Breathe out.

The police ushered us into our house, with Sergeant Dexter and a policewoman leading the way. I'd barely got my feet on our doormat before the front door was shut behind me. The unbearable roar was turned into a bearable din outside the door. And my swimmy, sick feeling faded. In spite of the ringing phone we all stood in the hall like statues. No one said a word.

'Well sir, welcome home!' said Sergeant Dexter drily.

Dad looked at him as if he was mad, then smiled slowly.

'Quite a homecoming,' he agreed. 'Are you all right, Cathy?'

Mum nodded. She headed for the ringing phone and picked it up. 'Hello?' she said.

I started to walk past her to go into the kitchen to get some water, but the changing expression on her face made me pause.

Pig Heart Boy by Malorie Blackman

1 Look at the paragraph beginning: *I could still hear them screaming at me.*

Explain why the writer has used a different style for the rest of this paragraph.

_____

2 What is the effect of writing, *On and on it went, on and on and on like a relentless tide?*

_____

_____

3 How is Cameron's idea of being famous different to the reality of being famous?

_____

_____

_____

_____

4 Explain what the phrase *rapt attention* tells you about the TV reporters.

_____

_____

5 Look at the paragraph beginning: *No, NO! ….*

In this paragraph, Cameron asks himself the questions: *What would Mum and Dad say? What would my friends say?*

What do these questions tell you about how Cameron is feeling?

_____

_____

6 Explain how the atmosphere changed once Cameron and his family were inside the house.

_____

_____

_____

_____

The story of Osiris

These questions will help you practise:
* ★ identifying key details from fiction
* ★ making comparisons
* ★ making inferences
* ★ explaining inferences
* ★ making predictions.

A long, long time ago, a special king was born in Egypt. His mother was the goddess of Heaven and his father the god of Earth. The king's name was Osiris and he was very wise. He taught his people how to live and work together, as well as how to understand the teachings of the gods.

Now Osiris married his sister, Isis, and they were very happy. This made their brother, Set, jealous – it seemed as if Osiris had everything. So Set thought of a plot to get rid of his brother. He ordered a beautiful wooden chest to be made to the king's measurements and promised it to whomever fitted inside most exactly. When Osiris tried it for size, Set's men immediately bolted the lid. They hurried away with the chest and threw it into the river Nile.

Meanwhile, Isis was kept prisoner by Set but she was determined to escape and find her husband's body. Isis tricked her captors and ran away in search of the chest. After many years of searching, she discovered it resting in the trunk of a tree, far away from home. Lovingly, she journeyed back with it to Egypt.

Set was seized with rage. He hunted down the chest and chopped Osiris' body into fourteen pieces, which he flung in every direction. But, fragment by fragment, Isis found and pieced together her husband's body. Carefully, she enclosed it in wax and bound it in linen cloths to make the first mummy. Then, using the magic teachings of Osiris, she summoned him back to life.

OSIRIS

Osiris rose to live forever in a peaceful land beyond the sky. Here, he judged the souls of the dead by weighing their hearts against a feather, called the Feather of Truth. Those whose hearts were heavy with bad deeds were fed to a hungry monster. But those whose hearts were as light as the feather were granted a new life in Osiris' happy kingdom.

First Puffin Book of Stories from World Religions by Annabel Shilson-Thomas

1 Number the events from **1** to **5** in the order in which they happen in the story.

Isis made the first mummy. ☐

Set plotted to get rid of Osiris. ☐

Osiris came back to life and lived in peace. ☐

Set chopped Osiris' body into small pieces. ☐

Isis set out to search for her husband. ☐

☐ 1
(1 mark)

2 What is different about Osiris' character compared to his brother, Set?
Give **two** examples, referring to the text.

_____

_____

☐ 2
(1 mark)

3 How do you know the wooden chest was made especially for the king?

_____

_____

☐ 3
(1 mark)

4 What conclusions can we come to about Isis' character?
Give **two** things about her character and support each with evidence from the text.

1. _____

_____

2. _____

_____

☐ 4
(2 marks)

5 Do you think Osiris forgave his brother?
Explain your answer fully, referring to the text.

_____

_____

_____

_____

_____

☐ 5
(3 marks)

/ 8
Total for
this text

The Anne Frank Exhibition

These questions will help you practise:
★ summarising main ideas
★ retrieving and recording information
★ identifying key details
★ making inferences
★ explaining inferences.

The following text is taken from an exhibition of family photographs taken by Otto Frank.

1926: Margot Betti Frank, born to Edith and Otto Frank, a Jewish family, in Frankfurt Am Main, Germany.

1929: Anneliese Marie (Anne) Frank, born in Frankfurt Am Main.

1933: Fearing Nazi anti-Semitism, the Franks decide to move to the Netherlands.

1934: Otto begins work in Amsterdam. The family move to Merwedeplein. Anne and Margot attend local schools and learn Dutch.

1936: Anne and Margot develop strong relationships with other children in their new neighbourhood.

1940: Following Nazi occupation, life in Amsterdam starts to change for the Franks.

1941: The Frank family have Nazi restrictions imposed on them. Anne and Margot are forced to change schools to the Jewish Lyceum.

1942: Grandmother Hollander dies. Anne receives her diary as a birthday gift. Margot is sent 'call-up' papers to report to a labour camp. The family move in to the 'secret annexe' prepared by Otto in his business premises. Anne takes her precious diary.

1943: Eight Jewish people are now hiding in the annexe, looked after by their brave helpers. Anne continues to write in her diary about daily life in hiding, her hopes, dreams and fears.

1944: On 1st August, Anne writes her last diary entry. Three days later the police raid the annexe. All those in hiding are imprisoned, then taken to Westerbork transit camp. One month later they are on the last transport to Auschwitz-Birkenau in Poland. Anne and Margot are moved to Bergen-Belsen camp.

1945: Anne is 15 years old when she, Margot and Edith perish in the concentration camps. Otto miraculously survives.

The Anne Frank Exhibition

1 Write **two** sentences to summarise the main ideas in this text.

_____

_____

_____

1
(1 mark)

2 Why did the Frank family move to Amsterdam?

_____

2
(1 mark)

3 When the family moved to Amsterdam, life continued as normal. Give **two** details to support this.

1. _____

2. _____

3
(2 marks)

4 How do you know that Margot and Anne settled in well when they moved to Merwedeplein?
Explain with reference to the text.

_____

4
(1 mark)

5 Match each event to the date it happened.

The family are found in the attic.	•	• 1940
Anne Frank is born.	•	• 1945
Anne, her sister and mother die.	•	• 1929
Anne receives a diary for her birthday.	•	• 1944
The Nazis occupy Amsterdam.	•	• 1942

5
(1 mark)

6 Explain how Anne might have felt about her diary.
Refer fully to the text in your answer.

_____

_____

_____

_____

_____

6
(3 marks)

/ 9

Total for this text

25

Footwear fashions

These questions will help you practise:
★ giving the meaning of words in context
★ retrieving and recording information
★ explaining how information contributes to meaning
★ making comparisons
★ summarising main ideas.

Fashion for the feet

Hunters were probably the first people to think of protecting their feet by wrapping them in animal skins – the earliest surviving examples date from the 2nd millennium BC. A Spanish cave painting of 13,000 BC depicted both a man and woman wearing boots of fur and animal skin. Gradually, however, boots became the essential footwear for men, while leisured women wore decorative but impractical shoes. Only in the 1830s did ankle boots – considered suitably modest – become fashionable for women.

In the 1820s the hero of Waterloo, the first Duke of Wellington, gave his name to a tall slim-cut leather boot. It reigned supreme until the 1860s, when it lost out to the elastic-sided boot, invented in 1837 by Queen Victoria's bootmaker, J Sparkes Hall, and reinvented in the 1950s as the Chelsea boot.

During the pre-Roman era, northern Europeans made shoes from a single piece of animal skin. They pierced the edges with holes, then threaded through a leather **thong**. This was pulled tight and tied on top of the foot. The Native American buckskin version, the *maxkeseni*, came to England in the 17th century as the moccasin and was briefly in vogue until it fell victim to an import tax.

The brogue, too, started out as a rough shoe of undressed leather tied on with thongs in 16th-century Ireland and Scotland. Holes allowed bog water to drain out while the wearer was walking. The shoe proved so practical that British gamekeepers and their masters adopted it, and by the late 1800s the shoe was heavier and square-toed. It became more refined until, in the 1930s, the Prince of Wales shocked conservative society by wearing suede brogues with a lounge suit.

Heights of fashion

In the late 11th century, shoemakers began to stitch together the sole and upper: previously, shoes had been made in one piece. Silk and velvet began to be used, while buttons and buckles became alternatives to laces when fastening footwear.

From the early Middle Ages, wooden clogs or *pattens* protected feet from Europe's filthy streets. In the 1500s, the Venetian *chopine* had a wedged sole that raised its wearer as much as 50 cm (20 in). Later in the 16th century, a more practical solution was made by building up layers of leather to form a wedge at the end of the sole, but by 1600 shoes had recognisable heels. As a result, it became more economical to make 'straights', which were worn on either foot and left and right shoes disappeared until the late 18th century.

The Curious History of Everyday Things
Reader's Digest

Glossary
• **thong** lace

1 *Gradually, however, boots became the essential footwear for men, while leisured women wore decorative but impractical shoes.*

What does the word *leisured* mean in this sentence?

_____

1 ☐
(1 mark)

2 Match the footwear to the date it was invented.

ankle boots	Middle Ages
wellington boots	1830s
moccasins	16th century
brogues	17th century
wooden clogs	1820s

2 ☐
(1 mark)

3 Explain why the writer has used **italic font** for some of the words in this text.

_____

_____

3 ☐
(1 mark)

4 Give **one** thing that is different about clogs, compared to the other footwear.

_____

_____

4 ☐
(1 mark)

5 How did the fastenings for shoes change?

_____

_____

5 ☐
(1 mark)

6 Using information from the text, tick one box in each row to show whether each statement is **true** or **false**.

	True	False
The Native American buckskin version was called a Chelsea boot.		
Silk and velvet were introduced in footwear in the 11th century.		
Heels were introduced in 1820.		
The Prince of Wales wore suede brogues with a lounge suit.		

6 ☐
(1 mark)

/ 6

Total for this text

Teddy and Kibbles

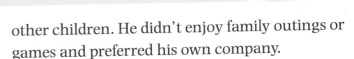

These questions will help you practise:
★ explaining the meaning of words in context
★ summarising main ideas
★ retrieving information and identifying key details
★ explaining inferences in non-fiction.

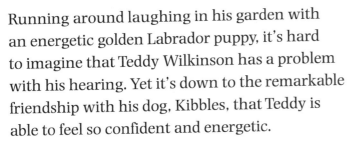

Running around laughing in his garden with an energetic golden Labrador puppy, it's hard to imagine that Teddy Wilkinson has a problem with his hearing. Yet it's down to the remarkable friendship with his dog, Kibbles, that Teddy is able to feel so confident and energetic.

Teddy was born with a hearing impairment in both his ears, which meant that he was unable to respond to the voices of his parents or any other noises around him.

"We knew something was wrong after a few weeks when we were calling his name and talking to him. He wasn't turning his head to look at us, or to any other sounds that were around. He didn't make the usual gurgling sounds that other babies were making," said his mother, Cathy.

After undergoing many tests and an operation to correct the impairment, it became obvious that Teddy's hearing was not going to improve significantly, though he did respond to some loud sounds and could make some noises.

"He loved dogs from an early age," said his dad, Thomas. "Although we didn't own a dog, my family have always kept dogs and Teddy responded to them all. The family dogs loved Teddy's company and we saw how he responded to their curiosity. Unfortunately, I'm allergic to dog hair!"

For four years, Teddy liked to be alone. He had very little confidence and wasn't interested in other children. He didn't enjoy family outings or games and preferred his own company.

"It was heart-breaking to see," said Thomas. "Teddy was a completely different child around the dogs. It was like he was a different boy."

The family decided to take immediate action. After lengthy discussion and many trips to an allergy specialist for Teddy's dad, the family bought Teddy a dog of his own.

"Kibbles was only a few months old when we bought him," said Cathy. The dog was very lively with sharp teeth and nails, but that didn't worry Teddy, who was only four years old at the time.

Within days, Teddy was laughing, pointing and shouting in his own way. Despite difficulties with speech and hearing, communication with his family and the children in his class improved. Teddy even took Kibbles to school to visit his classmates.

Teddy and Kibbles are inseparable, Kibbles acting as Teddy's own 'hearing dog'. Now six years old, Teddy has taught Kibbles to do many of the usual tricks dogs can do, such as fetch a ball, sit and stay. He has even taught Kibbles to tell him to come in when his tea is ready.

"It's the start of his life," said Cathy, "and a friendship that will last forever. Thanks to Kibbles, Teddy feels confident and positive. He's like any other mischievous little boy!" As for Teddy's dad, thanks to modern medicine, there's no more sneezes and itching in the house!

Answers and mark scheme

The snow spider (pages 6–7)

1 2a – 1 mark. It means he wanted all his grandmother's attention for himself.
He wanted his grandmother to focus on him and nothing else.

2 2g – 2 marks for developed answer. It compares her eyes to a child's eyes and tells you that her eyes were wide open with excitement just like a child's would be when they saw something new or exciting.
1 mark for undeveloped answer. It tells you that she was excited and was staring.

3 2g – 1 mark. To tell the reader that Gwyn wasn't quite sure what it was / hadn't seen anything like it before.

4 2b – 1 mark. 'But did I make it, Nain?' or: Gwyn watched and felt that it was Nain who was the magician and he the enchanted one.

5 2b – 1 mark for a correctly identified simile, e.g. and there it rested, shining like a star beneath her wild black curls.

6 2g – 1 mark. To emphasise how cross / worried Nain was at the suggestion that Gwyn take the spider to a museum. / To ensure that Gwyn got the message that he must not take the spider to the museum.

7 2b – 2 marks. 1 mark each for any two of the following:
She gave an ecstatic gasp when she saw it. / Her eyes sparkled like a child's. / She took the spider and placed it on her arm. / She danced while the spider crawled up her sleeve.

Comfort at the market (pages 8–9)

1 2a – 1 mark. It explains the intensity of the market noise, like: a din, uproar, commotion, confusion.

2 2b – Award 3 marks for two examples and fully developed answers with reference to the text: The sounds of the market are constant / shrill / loud; echoed back means they would have been repetitive and ongoing. The sights of the market suggest a busy atmosphere, where people are constantly greeting and calling to each other, lorries are coming and going and customers are browsing the stalls.
Award 2 marks for two examples and developed answer: The market is noisy and the sounds are constant with people calling. The market is a busy sight with lots of movement from people and lorries.
Award 1 mark for two examples only, or one example developed: It's loud and busy.

3 2d – 1 mark. Comfort is Ata's niece. It says that she is the 'child of my brother, Mante'.

4 2d – 1 mark. She was anxious because, despite being given medicine, Bolo wasn't getting any better.

5 2g – 1 mark. To compare the way in which Comfort is looking at the activity of the market, in the same way in which an owl might stare at the activity of creatures scuttling on the ground. / To compare the size of Comfort's eyes as she stares at the market, not quite understanding what is going on, with an owl's wide eyes, staring at the activity of scuttling creatures.

6 2d – 2 marks. 1 mark each for two examples, such as: By describing things that are unfamiliar or unusual in this country, such as women sitting on the ground with baskets containing fruits that don't grow in this country, such as oranges, yams, cassava. The babies were tied to the backs of their mothers.

The mysterious bones (pages 10–11)

1 2c – 1 mark. Danny has found a part of a skeleton in the leat and thinks it's the skeleton of a murdered man, so he and Tyke run down to look at it.

2 2f – 1 mark for any of the following: One of the lines is from a song. The other two are a joke. They are different to the story. / Danny is singing a song and tells Tyke a joke before the story begins. / To separate the song and joke from the story.

3 2b – 1 mark for each detail.
1 Tyke tells Danny that the bones weren't there last week.
2 He tells him that they are a sheep's bones like the one Martin Kneeshaw found and he repeats it.

4 2a – 1 mark for all correctly written: skeleton / who's been murdered / brought

5 2d – 1 mark – Tyke. The story is written in the first person using the words I, me, we, etc. We know the narrator is called Tyke because Danny says 'It's lovely, Tyke' and 'It's a real skellinton, Tyke' when talking to the narrator.

6 2e / 2h – 2 marks. Tyke might take it out of the water just to prove it is a sheep as Danny doesn't believe him. Danny might call the police because he really believes it is the remains of a dead body and he didn't believe it was a sheep skeleton.

Underwater peace (pages 12–13)

1 2f – 1 mark. To create a sense of a calming atmosphere. / To give the illusion that beneath the water it is silent and peaceful. / To create a sense of calm in contrast to the long, dramatic and loud sentences before them. / To make the reader slow down, which may have a calming effect on the reader.

2 2g – 1 mark. A simile is used to create the idea of the thunderous / growling sound of the blood as it moves through his body in a similar way to the sound of the roar of an angry monster.

3 2h – Award 3 marks for fully developed answers referring to the text and both characters:
Marlon is a worrier. He is concerned that Cam was sitting under the water and is at the poolside instead of being at his house. He is worried Cam's parents will find out and they'll get into trouble.
Cam is a risk taker. He knows he shouldn't be at the pool or under the water, but is doing it anyway regardless of Marlon's advice. Cam is irritable. Marlon feels hurt.

Award 2 marks for fully developed answers with reference to one of the characters:

Marlon is a worrier. He is concerned that Cam was sitting under the water and is at the poolside instead of being at his house. He is worried Cam's parents will find out and they'll get into trouble.

Cam is a risk taker. He knows he shouldn't be at the pool or under the water, but is doing it anyway regardless of Marlon's advice.

Award 1 mark for undeveloped answers referring to both characters: Cam is a risk taker. Marlon is a worrier.

4 2b – 1 mark each for any two of the following: He asked Cam if he *was all right.* / He wondered whether it was a good idea for him to *sit down* under water. / He told Cam he *shouldn't be under water.* / Marlon *clucks* over Cam.

5 2d – Award 3 marks for developed answers with reference to the text: Cam is not in good health. At the beginning of the text, he sat under the water to get away from the noise. His lungs were aching and he had a sharp stabbing pain in his chest. He could feel the blood roaring in his ears. / Marlon is concerned for Cam throughout the text which suggests Cam has health problems.

Award 2 marks for developed answers: Cam is not in good health because it says he had a pain in his chest. / His lungs ache.

Award 1 mark for undeveloped answer: Cam is not well. / Cam is not in good health.

6 2c – Award 1 mark for all three correct: true / false / false

Krishna fights the Serpent King (pages 14–15)

1 2a – 1 mark. He ruled / governed / reigned / controlled.

2 2f – 1 mark. To show the power and size of the serpent. / To describe the size and scale of the destruction and devastation he can cause.

3 a) 2g – 1 mark – *a simile.*
   b) 2g – 1 mark for answers about it showing that Kaliya is in pain / under pressure / being overwhelmed by the huge power of Krishna.

4 2b – 1 mark for all correctly ordered:
Krishna landed on the heads of the serpent. *4*
Krishna's friends were drowned. *3*
Kaliya killed the blacksmith's son. *2*
The serpent burnt the countryside. *1*
Kaliya returned to his court. *5*

5 2h – 1 mark for answers relating to what Kaliya or Krishna will do: Kaliya will drag Krishna below the water and try to drown him in his whirlpool home, hoping that Krishna won't be able to breathe. / Kaliya will rise up, shooting flames around Krishna before dragging him below the water. / Krishna will summon all his courage and powers and defeat the serpent.

6 2d – 1 mark for any of the following: Kaliya felt as if all the mountains of the Himalayas were raining on his head. / Krishna crushed one of Kaliya's heads under one arm and another head under another arm. / He danced on the remaining three heads. / Krishna defeated Kaliya.

Dangerous visitors (pages 16–17)

1 2d – 1 mark. He says, '*They have come. I feared they might*' which means that he had predicted their arrival.

2 2a – 1 mark – reason

3 2b – Award 3 marks for developed answers with reference to the text: They have come to make peace with Arthur, yet Merlin knows it was Arthur who gave the order for their husbands to be killed. It seems strange / odd that they should want to make peace with the person who ordered the deaths of their husbands. The text asks, why should they love him?

Award 2 marks for developed answers: Merlin knows it would be hard for them to make peace with the person who ordered the deaths of their husbands.

Award 1 mark for undeveloped answer: Their husbands have been killed because of Arthur.

4 2b – 1 mark. *a ... shiver came over him; Merlin's eyes narrowed; he had to lean against the ramparts to steady himself.*

5 2a – 1 mark. To show that as he gets older his powers are weakening / vanishing / disappearing.

6 2c – 1 mark. Answers related to what Merlin has told Arthur so far: I want to know who the child is. / I wonder if the child is mine. / I wonder if the women are here to kill me. / I fear there is something threatening my future. / I hope Merlin can predict my future.

Treasure Island (pages 18–19)

1 2c – 1 mark. Answers related to the transportation and seizure of the gold from the island to the ship, e.g. The movement of the gold. / The gold is moved / transported to the ship. / Booty from shore to ship.

2 a) 2g – 1 mark – To autumn leaves
   b) 2g – 2 marks for developed answer (with or without the identification of a simile): It is a simile which compares the way in which the coins are scattered on the floor like autumn leaves scattered on the ground because he had to bend down to pick them up. / To describe the way in which the coins are scattered on the floor like autumn leaves that have fallen to the ground. His back ached from picking them up.
   1 mark for undeveloped answer: The coins are lying on the floor like leaves.

3 2b – 1 mark for all correctly ordered:
Treasure was put in piles. *4*
The coins were sorted out. *2*
Two men sailed the boat to the ship and back. *5*
The coins were put into bread-bags. *3*
A soldier kept watch on the hill. *1*

4 2f – 1 mark. The coins have come from all over the world.

5 2d – Award 3 marks for fully developed answer referring to the text: No, it wasn't easy. It says it was a considerable task for a few people which means it was difficult as the gold was heavy. Only two bars of gold at a time could be carried in a rope by one man walking slowly. Even sorting out the coins made one man's back and fingers ache.

Award 2 marks for fully developed answer: No. The gold was heavy. One man could only carry two bars of gold and they had to take it a long way to get to the ship. Award 1 mark for an undeveloped answer: No. The gold was heavy and it took a long time to move it slowly to the beach.

Cameron faces the press (pages 20–21)

1 2f – 1 mark. To show the TV reporters calling to Cameron. / To show the difference between the TV reporters shouting and the rest of the story.

2 2g – 1 mark. To give the impression that the calling is repetitive and never-ending, like a tide that is on a continual / never-ending cycle.

3 2d – Award up to 3 marks for fully developed response with reference to the text: Because of his experience of seeing famous pop stars surrounded by fans on TV, Cameron was expecting his fame to be fun. However, in reality, Cameron feels that it is terrifying being surrounded and shouted at for his attention. This means that he realises being famous is not as much fun as he'd hoped.
Award up to 2 marks for developed response: He thought it was fun, but he realises the attention is really terrifying and not fun at all.
Award 1 mark for undeveloped response: It is terrifying. / It is not fun.

4 2a – 1 mark. It tells you the reporters' attention was completely focused on Cameron. / They were gripped / focused / absorbed / could not take their attention away.

5 2d – 1 mark. To show that Cameron is fearful of his friends and parents seeing him do something he would be ashamed of / embarrassed by. / He is telling himself that he should not faint under any circumstances to avoid embarrassment and shame.

6 2g – Award up to 3 marks for fully developed response with reference to both inside and outside the house: The atmosphere changed from one of constant noise and activity outside the house to one of quiet and calm inside the house. The noise from outside has stopped and it is quieter – *The unbearable roar was turned into a bearable din.* No one spoke or moved – *we all stood in the hall like statues.*
Cameron's feeling of sickness disappeared in the calmer atmosphere – the *swimmy, sick feeling faded.* Dad had stopped yelling at the reporters and was smiling.
Award up to 2 marks for developed response with reference to inside the house: It was much quieter. The din had faded and Cameron didn't feel sick any more because he felt calmer.
Award 1 mark for undeveloped response to inside the house: It was quieter indoors than outside.

The story of Osiris (pages 22–23)

1 2c – 1 mark for all numbers correctly ordered:
Isis made the first mummy. *4*
Set plotted to get rid of Osiris. *1*
Osiris came back to life and lived in peace. *5*
Set chopped Osiris' body into small pieces. *3*
Isis set out to search for her husband. *2*

2 2h – 1 mark for developed answers including two pieces of evidence from text: Osiris is a wise king. He teaches his people how to live in peace and to understand the gods. / Set is evil and jealous. He sets out to remove his brother from his kingdom by killing him. / When Osiris comes back to life, he lives in peace and grants people with happy hearts a place in his kingdom. / Set imprisons Isis so she can't search for her husband.

3 2d – 1 mark. Only the king's body fitted the chest. / Set *ordered a beautiful wooden chest to be made to the king's measurements.*

4 2d – Award 2 marks, one for each correct answer. Any two of the following: Isis was heroic and strong-minded. She was determined to find her husband. / She was clever – she managed to outwit the guards and escape. / Isis was a loving wife. It took her years to find her husband's body. / She pieced his body together.

5 2e – Award up to 3 marks for fully developed answers referring to the text with reasons: Yes. Osiris was a kind and wise king. He wanted peace and taught people the ways of the gods. When he returned he lived in a peaceful land and judged people's actions. He would have forgiven his brother because he was his family. / No, because when he returned, he judged people by their actions. *Those whose hearts were heavy with bad deeds were fed to a hungry monster*, so that's what might have happened to Set.
Award up to 2 marks for developed answers: Yes, because he wanted people to live and work together so he might have given Set another chance. / No, because he fed bad people to a monster so he probably fed Set to it too.
Award 1 mark for undeveloped answer: Yes, because he was a kind person. / No, because he fed bad people to a monster.

The Anne Frank Exhibition (pages 24–25)

1 2c – 1 mark for both answers. One answer should be related to the life of the family during occupation. For example: The girls growing up in occupied Amsterdam. / The family hiding from the Nazis. / Family life going on during the occupation.
The second answer should be related to the deaths in the family and the survival of Mr Frank. For example: Despite moving and hiding, all members of the Frank family died except Mr Frank. / When they were found, the family were moved to a camp where the girls and their mother died. / The only surviving member of the family was Mr Frank.

2 2b – 1 mark. To escape from the Nazis in Germany. / They were Jewish and had to flee from Nazi occupation.

3 2b – Award 2 marks, one for each detail. Any two of the following: Otto Frank started work. / Anne and Margot started local schools. / Anne and Margot learned to speak Dutch. / The girls made friends in the neighbourhood.

4 2d – 1 mark. They developed *strong relationships with other children in their new neighbourhood.*/They made friends quickly where they lived./They made good friends quickly when they moved.

5 2b – 1 mark for all lines drawn correctly:
The family are found in the attic. – 1944
Anne Frank is born. – 1929
Anne, her sister and mother die. – 1945
Anne receives a diary for her birthday. – 1942
The Nazis occupy Amsterdam. – 1940

6 2d – Award 3 marks for fully developed response with reference to the text: Anne thought her diary was very important/dear to her. The text says that it was *precious*. She took the diary with her when they had to hide in the secret annexe. When you have important things you look after them and you might take them with you. She wrote in her diary every day and included her hopes, dreams and fears, things that were very personal to her.
Award 2 marks for developed response with reference to the text: Anne's diary was really important to her. It was *precious*. She took it to the annexe with her and wrote in it every day.
Award 1 mark for undeveloped response: The diary was important to Anne.

Footwear fashions (pages 26–27)

1 2a – 1 mark – rich; wealthy; well-off; not having to work

2 2b – 1 mark for all lines drawn correctly:
ankle boots – 1830s
wellington boots – 1820s
moccasins – 17th century
brogues – 16th century
wooden clogs – Middle Ages

3 2f – 1 mark. For the technical/real names of the footwear; to show that these words are unusual/unfamiliar either because they are foreign (e.g. *maxkeseni* and *chopine*) or are old-fashioned (e.g. *pattens*).

4 2h – 1 mark for reference to either of these points:
Clogs were made of wood/other shoes were made of animal skins, leather, included embellishments such as satin and buttons.

5 2b – 1 mark. Buttons and buckles replaced laces.

6 2c – Award 1 mark for all four correct:
false/true/false/true

Teddy and Kibbles (pages 28–29)

1 2a – 1 mark – It was amazing/incredible/astonishing.

2 2c – 1 mark – *helped him gain confidence.*

3 2f – 1 mark – *curiosity*

4 2b – 1 mark for all five correctly answered:
fact/fact/opinion/fact/opinion

5 2h – Award 2 marks for reference to how he was before and how he is now.
He had no confidence. Now he is confident and positive./He preferred his own company. Now he shows Kibbles to his classmates and has Kibbles to play with.
Award 1 mark for how he was or how he is now.

He had no confidence./He played on his own./He had no friends.
He is confident and positive./He shows Kibbles to his classmates./He has Kibbles to play with.

6 2d – Award 2 marks for more than one reason from the following:
It helped him to communicate better with other people. He had a new friend, which made him feel happy. He was keen to communicate with his classmates and he took the dog in to see them. He no longer played on his own.
Award 1 mark for any one reason.

The mobile phone debate (pages 30–31)

1 2a – 1 mark – (Educational) researchers; professors; lecturers; teachers; tutors.

2 2b – 1 mark – Nottingham University

3 2b – 2 marks. 1 mark each for any two of the following:
They were used to create short films, set homework reminders, record a teacher reading a poem and time experiments with the phones' stopwatches. To access revision websites, log into the school email system, or transfer electronic files between school and home.

4 2c – 1 mark for a suitable headline as a question or statement relating to the debate, e.g. Mobile phones in school? You decide: Should mobile phones be used in schools?

5 2b – 2 marks. 1 mark each for any two of the following words in bold (which must be written on their own or as part of a phrase or sentence): a study **claims**…; trials **suggested** that…; some teachers **think**…; I **thought**…; we **believe** that….

6 2d – Award 3 marks for a fully developed, text-based explanation for both positive and negative outcomes. Award 2 marks for a fully developed, text-based explanation of either a positive or a negative outcome. Award 1 mark for two undeveloped points.
Positive outcomes:
Learning in school, e.g. timing experiments; recording lessons; creating films.
Home communication, e.g. homework reminders can be set; email between home and school can be accessed.
Negative outcomes:
Misuse: temptation to cyber-bully; cheat in tests; theft of phones; use of inappropriate images.
Data protection: data and security risks; sharing or gaining access to private information.

Snow shelters (pages 32–33)

1 a) 2f – 1 mark. To give instructions./To tell you how to make something.
   b) 2f – 2 marks. 1 mark each for two of the following features: numbered paragraphs; imperative/command verbs; present tense; diagrams.

2 a) 2b – 2 marks. 1 mark for each word – *essential* and *vital*
   b) 2b – 1 mark. To emphasise the importance of the given information./To warn/emphasise to the reader the importance of following the instructions carefully to avoid serious consequences.

3 2g – 1 mark. To give additional information about the temperature, length, height and depth. / To give additional information for those people who still use imperial measures.

4 2d – Award 3 marks for a fully developed, text-based explanation with reasoning: For children – it says it only takes a few hours to build if the temperature remains below zero so they might need help. For explorers or people who venture to very cold climates and need to protect themselves from the cold – the text includes technical vocabulary on ventilation and gases which adults would understand.
Award 2 marks for a developed, text-based explanation: For children because it would be fun to make an igloo. For explorers who travel to the Arctic and need a shelter.
Award 1 mark for an undeveloped point: Children and explorers.

The travels of Marianne North (pages 34–35)

1 a) 2a – 1 mark – *exquisite*
  b) 2a – 1 mark – *mode*

2 a) 2g – 1 mark for one of the following similes:
  1 *scarlet erythrinas looking like gems*;
  2 *the pistil … was curved like the spring of a watch.*
  b) 2g – 1 mark for the effect.
  1 The effect is to create an image of the colour of the plant, to show how the colour is similar to the colour of gems. / The effect is to show how the colours of the plant shone / sparkled in the sun like gemstones.
  2 The effect is to create an image of how the middle of the flower moves. The movement happens in the same way as a watch spring.

3 2a – 1 mark – eye-catching; obvious; noticeable; on show

4 2h – 1 mark. In Australia it was wet; raining. In India it was *neither too hot nor too cold*; it was just right; cloudless sky / sun.

5 2b – 1 mark – Brazil

6 2d – Award 3 marks for a fully developed, text-based explanation with reasons: A biologist or someone interested in exotic plants and flowers. The writer is in the tropics and there are many descriptions of tropical plants with some of their Latin names such as erythrina and loranthus which means she would have studied biology or Latin maybe. / An explorer / traveller as she enjoys visiting far off and unusual places in the world which would not have been explored at that time by many people.
Award 2 marks for a developed, text-based explanation: An artist or biologist who wants to paint exotic flowers. / An explorer who wants to travel all over the world.
Award 1 mark for an undeveloped point: an artist; an explorer; a plant collector.

Dumping waste in the sea (pages 36–37)

1 2c – 1 mark. Continual dumping of millions of tons of plastics in the sea is polluting the water and killing and endangering sea life.

2 2a – 1 mark – shocking; incredible; overwhelming; unbelievable

3 2b – 2 marks. 1 mark each for the following: amount of waste and how well it is disposed of.

4 2b – 1 mark for all five correctly answered: opinion / fact / fact / opinion / opinion

5 2d – 1 mark – *to explain and inform*

6 2d – Award 3 marks for a fully developed, text-based explanation:
The oceans will become so polluted that there will be no wildlife left. It says that eight million tons of plastic end up in the oceans each year.
We won't be able to eat food from the oceans because it might have been polluted by the plastics. It says that it could harm our health to eat fish that have consumed plastic. Animals could become extinct if they keep dying from the pollution.
Award 2 marks for a developed, text-based explanation: The amount of plastic will keep endangering the wildlife. Humans might be harmed if they eat the fish.
Award 1 mark for an undeveloped point: The plastic will keep polluting the sea. / The plastic will keep killing the animals. / Humans might die.

How to make a double helix (pages 38–39)

1 a) 2f – 1 mark. To give instructions. / To tell you how to make something.
  b) 2f – 2 marks. 1 mark for any two of these features: what you need listed in bullet points; numbered paragraphs; imperative / command verbs; present tense.

2 2b – Award 1 mark for any of the following facts: Almost all organisms have a 'genetic fingerprint'. / DNA molecules hold information about an organism's inherited traits. / DNA molecules can copy themselves.

3 2b – 1 mark – *in chronological order*

4 2b – 1 mark – *template*

5 a) 2b – 1 mark for three of the following – *curl, follow, make, mould, thread, wrap,* etc.
  b) 2g – 1 mark. They tell you what to do in a brief way.

Jousting (pages 40–41)

1 a) 2f – 1 mark. To give information about jousting.
  b) 2f – 2 marks. 1 mark each for any two of the following features: heading; introduction in bold font; sub-headings; information arranged in paragraphs; technical vocabulary; unknown vocabulary in bold font; question / fact box; language of cause and effect (*because, if*).

2 2a – 1 mark – announcement; statement; message; declaration; notice

3 2g – Award 3 marks for two responses with reference to the text:
  1 By giving a direct explanation after the words, such as '*joust a plaisance*' and a '*pas d'armes*'.
  2 By giving the English interpretation in brackets after the French words, such as *tinctures* (colours), *ordinaires* (layout designs).

Award 2 marks for one response with reference to the text: By giving the English interpretation in brackets after the French words, such as *tinctures* (colours), *ordinaires* (layout designs).

Award 1 mark for one response with no reference to the text: By giving the English words in brackets after the French words.

4   2b – 1 mark. They took part in many contests which took place over many days until a winner was found.

5   2d – 1 mark. For people who are interested in how knights lived in medieval times and what jousting tournaments consisted of. / For people who are going to watch or who have watched a mock jousting tournament at a castle and want to understand the background behind them.
Do not accept: For people who are interested in jousting.

6   2h – Award 3 marks for fully developed response: The information in the box explains that knights in battle mostly died from diseases, which means that they became ill more often. At that time, there was not good health care / medicines as there are today, so even though knights were brave and strong, they were not strong enough to fight diseases.
Award 2 marks for developed response: They died from diseases more, which means they weren't as strong as they might have thought.
Award 1 mark for undeveloped points: They weren't as strong as they thought. / They could not fight diseases.

The life of Adrian Henri (pages 42–43)

1   2b – 2 marks. 1 mark each for any two details:
carrying gas mask to school every day;
aircraft-recognition charts pinned to my bedroom wall;
the smell of paint on toy soldiers; doing paintings of Spitfires and Hurricanes, Lancasters and Halifaxes; clutching my father's hand.

2   2d – 1 mark – aeroplanes (also accept bombs)

3   2g – 1 mark – smell – it says that he smells paint; hearing – it says that he listens for the all clear, Vera Lynn (singers / bands).

4   2f – 1 mark. To show that the memories are happening at the present, in his thoughts. / To show that the memories are current, as if they are happening now.

5   2g – Award 3 marks for fully developed text-based explanation for two or more reasons related to safety from danger: He kept himself safe from the danger of air attacks during the war by following instructions / doing what he was told. The poem says that he did the things that children would have had to do to protect themselves during the war such as: wore his tin hat in case things fell on him; carried his gas mask in case there was a gas attack; avoided careless talk by not spreading gossip; going to the air-raid shelter when there was an air raid; holding his father's hand in the black-out so he didn't trip up.
Award 2 marks for fully developed explanation with at least two examples from the text: He protected his head

by wearing a tin hat; carrying his gas mask; going in the air-raid shelter; holding his dad's hand.
Award 1 mark for one or two undeveloped points: It tells you he was safe because he wore his hat and carried his mask.

6   2d – 1 mark. That the pavement is changing daily because of the bombing so it is never the same.

Pleasant sounds (pages 44–45)

1   2b – 1 mark – *brown leaves*

2   a) 2g – 1 mark – *rustling* (of leaves), *crumping* (of cat-ice), *whizzing* (of birds), *pattering* (of nuts), etc.
b) 2g – 1 mark for the effect. To create an image of the wood as a place full of sounds; as a noisy place; as a place that is not quiet.

3   2g – 1 mark for a correctly found and copied example of alliteration, e.g. *The crumping of cat-ice.*

4   a) 2g – 1 mark for *while the wind halloos in the oak-top like thunder.*
b) 2g – 1 mark for effect: To exaggerate the loud noise of the wind in the same way as a loud clap of thunder. / The wind greeting the oak tree in a really noisy way in the same way as a loud clap of thunder.

5   2c / 2d – Award 3 marks for fully developed text-based explanation: Answers related to the season or the sounds.
Title: 'Autumn Sights' because the poem contains things that can be seen or felt in nature in autumn, such as leaves, robins and woodlarks, acorns and nuts, thin ice on the ground and cold wind.
Title: 'Sounds of Autumn' because the poem contains things that could be heard in nature in autumn, such as: *the rustling of leaves; the trample of robins … on the brown leaves; the fall of an acorn on the ground; nuts on the hazel branches as they fall from ripeness; the sound of the wind through the oak tops.*
Award 2 marks for fully developed explanation:
'Autumn Sights' – The poem gives examples of things you see in autumn, such as leaves falling, nuts, acorns and sometimes ice.
'Sounds of Autumn' – The poem is full of sounds you might hear in autumn, such as rustling and trampling.
Award 1 mark for undeveloped points:
'Autumn Sights' – Leaves fall off the trees. Acorns fall down.
'Autumn Sounds' – rustling, trampling, blowing.

The magic of the brain (pages 46–47)

1   2d – 1 mark – the senses: sight, sound, smell, touch, taste (all five should be included).

2   2d – 1 mark. From the warmth of the fur of the pet on her lap.

3   2d – 1 mark. The writer is using the sense of smell. The fourth line uses the word *fragrance* – *Jellies and puddings and fragrance of fruit they are made from.* Fragrance is something that you smell.

4   2f – 1 mark. To introduce the ideas relating to the sense used, which will follow in the verse. / To introduce the list of things that the writer senses in the verse.

5   2d – 1 mark. *Lifted my heart; cleared my head; breathed content.*

6   2g – 1 mark. To show an appreciation of how the objects in each verse make the writer feel through her senses./To show how delighted the writer is by experiencing the objects through her senses./To show how important the experiences in each verse are to the writer./To give the poem a structure./To link the verses together.

7   2c – 1 mark. To show that by using the senses, you can experience different things in the world/bring the world into your life./To show how the senses allow you to experience different things in the world./To show that your brain, which is in control of your senses, can bring experiences of the world into your life.

The harvest (pages 48–49)

1   2c – 1 mark for any suggested title that makes sense in the context of the poem, e.g. A Childhood Memory/Late August/The Hoard in the Byre/A Summer Ritual.

2   a) 2g – 1 mark – *thickened wine*
    b) 2g – 1 mark. It is effective because it makes the reader imagine the taste of the ripe berries and the way the juice would feel in your mouth.

3   2f – 2 marks. 1 mark each for any two of the following: first person singular (*I, you*) and plural pronouns (*we, us*); information/facts about the day; both present and past tenses.

4   2a – 1 mark – hoard; stash; store; supply

5   2f/2g – Award 3 marks for fully developed answer referring to place and time of year: The writer builds a picture of the setting by: stating where and when the poem is set – in summer, in *August* in *hayfields* and *byres*, which means that it must be in the countryside or in and around a farm when the weather was hot.
    Award 2 marks for fully developed answer: In the countryside in the summer beside *hayfields* and *byres*.
    Award 1 mark for undeveloped points: Beside blackberry bushes in *hayfields*.

6   2h – Award 2 marks for comparisons at the beginning and at the end: At the beginning, they are red and glossy. At the end, they have fungus on them./At the beginning, the flesh was sweet. At the end, the flesh was sour.
    Award 1 mark for one description at the beginning or at the end: At the beginning, they were sweet./At the end, they were sour./At the beginning, they are red and glossy./At the end, they have fungus on them./At the beginning, the flesh was sweet./At the end, the flesh was sour.

Stop all the clocks (pages 50–51)

1   2d – 1 mark. The death of someone the writer loved very much./The death of the writer's partner/husband.

2   2a – 1 mark. A funeral goer; a friend or relative of the dead person.

3   a) 2g – 2 marks. 1 mark each for any two of the following: *Stop, Prevent, Silence, Bring, Cut off, Let.*

b) 2g – 1 mark. The effect of the command verbs is that they show the writer is serious/means business.

4   2h – Award 1 mark for the following point: In the first verse, the focus is on everyday things (objects/people – clocks, telephone, dog, bone, pianos, drum, coffin, mourners). The focus in the fourth verse is on objects from nature/natural phenomena, such as the stars, the moon and the sun.
    There is also a change of scale; the first verse deals with immediate, small-scale things whereas the fourth verse deals with large-scale things.

5   2g – 1 mark for a correctly copied metaphor, e.g. *My noon, my midnight, my talk, my song.*

6   2d – Award up to 3 marks for a fully developed text-based explanation for both a possible and an impossible demand. For example:
    Some of the writer's demands aren't possible. Some of the things in the poem are everyday events that cannot be stopped, such as natural occurrences in the universe, like the stars, the sun, the moon, the oceans. These are things that are out of the control of people.
    It is possible to stop people talking, stop clocks from ticking by pulling out the plug or batteries; dogs could be stopped from barking by giving them a bone to chew.
    Award up to 2 marks for fully developed text-based explanation of either a possible or an impossible demand:
    The demands about things in the universe aren't possible because these are things that are out of our control. Some demands are possible, such as giving a dog a bone to stop it from barking.
    Award 1 mark for two undeveloped points:
    Yes, you can stop clocks from working. No, you can't stop the moon from coming out.

The Pied Piper of Hamelin (pages 52–53)

1   2a – 1 mark – *strangest*

2   2g – 2 marks. 1 mark for each reason: The purpose is to create a more dramatic vision/description of the Piper's strange/different appearance.

3   2b – 2 marks. 1 mark for each example, including: *kith, kin, attire, quoth.*

4   2a – 1 mark. It is appropriate because it gives a clear idea of the high-pitched/ear-piercing or sharp sound produced by the Piper's pipe.

5   2g – 1 mark. To give the reader an image of how the Piper's eyes danced/sparkled/twinkled./To show that the blue-green colour of the Piper's eyes was the same colour as a flame when salt is sprinkled into it.

6   a) 2f – 1 mark – *reads quickly.*
    b) 2f – 1 mark. To imagine the continuous speed at which the rats came tumbling out of buildings./
    To show the rats constantly/continuously spilling/tumbling out of buildings onto the streets without stopping.

Night mail (pages 54–55)

1 2c – 1 mark. A train is driving through the night to deliver mail to people in Scotland who will be sleeping when it arrives.

2 2g – 1 mark for correctly identifying an example of alliteration: *Shovelling, Snorting, Silent, Stare.*

3 2g – 1 mark. To remind the reader that the train is a mail train and is constantly carrying all different kinds of letters from different people to different people and to different places./The mail train repeats this journey regularly, carrying all different kinds of letters from different people to different people and to different places.

4 a) 2f – 1 mark. The rhythm speeds up/increases.

   b) 2f – Award 3 marks for fully developed answer with reference to the text: The effect is to match the rhythm of the poem/speed at which the reader reads, to the increased pace/movement of the train as it *descends* rapidly to *Glasgow* from high up in *Beattock.*
   Award 2 marks for fully developed answer: To match the speed of reading the poem to the speed that the train is travelling as it gets quicker.
   Award 1 mark for undeveloped points: To read quickly like the speed of the train.
   Do not accept: to make you/the reader read quickly.

5 2h – Award 3 marks for fully developed answer with reference to both parts of the text: Answers related to the countryside/city: the noises; daytime and night time. The first section suggests that the setting is in the countryside as the poem makes reference to miles of wind-bent grasses and sheep dogs asleep. The train also passes a farm. In the second section, the train passes steam tugs and cranes, apparatus and furnaces which suggest this is a town or a city.

In the first section, it is quiet as the train is travelling through the night. The only sound that can be heard is the sound of the steam. The poem says that sheep dogs are asleep and no one wakes from the sound of the train at the farm that it passes. The second section is noisier with the sound of the steam tugs which 'yelp' and you can imagine the sound of the people working the cranes.
Award 2 marks for developed answer with reference to one part of the text:
The first section is in the countryside because there is a farm mentioned.
The second section is noisy because of the sounds of the steam tugs.
Award 1 mark for reference to any of the following points:
The first one is in the country/the second one is in a city/town.
The first one is quiet/the second one is noisier.
The first one is during the night/the second one is during the day.

1 Look at the sentence beginning: *Yet it's down to the remarkable friendship with his dog, Kibbles….*

What does the word *remarkable* tell you about their friendship?

_____

1
(1 mark)

2 The main idea the text gives about Teddy is that his bond with Kibbles…

Tick one.

gave him friends at school. ☐

stopped his dad from sneezing. ☐

helped him gain confidence. ☐

helped him teach Kibbles tricks. ☐

2
(1 mark)

3 Look at the paragraph beginning: *He loved dogs from an early age….*

Find and **copy** the word which explains that the dogs were interested in Teddy.

_____

3
(1 mark)

4 Tick one box in each row to show whether each statement is a **fact** or an **opinion**.

	Fact	Opinion
Teddy was born with damage to his ears.		
Teddy played on his own.		
The puppy's sharp teeth didn't worry Teddy.		
Kibbles can bring a ball back to Teddy.		
Teddy is a mischievous boy.		

4
(1 mark)

5 Give **one** thing that is different about Teddy now compared to how he was before he had Kibbles.

_____

5
(2 marks)

6 How did playing with Kibbles help Teddy to become more confident?

_____

6
(2 marks)

/ 8

Total for
this text

29

The mobile phone debate

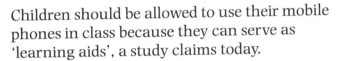

These questions will help you practise:
★ giving the meaning of words in context
★ retrieving and recording information
★ summarising main ideas
★ making inferences
★ explaining inferences.

Children should be allowed to use their mobile phones in class because they can serve as 'learning aids', a study claims today.

Academics are calling on schools to rethink bans on phone handsets after trials suggested that functions such as calculators, stopwatches and email can be 'educational'.

However, the call is certain to infuriate many teachers and parents, who will be concerned that pupils will be unable to resist the temptation to put the devices to less productive uses, such as cyber-bullying or cheating in tests.

During a nine-month experiment involving classes aged 14 to 16, pupils either used their own mobiles in lessons or the new generation of 'smartphones' which allow internet connection.

They were used to create short films, set homework reminders, record a teacher reading a poem and time experiments with the phones' stopwatches.

The smartphones also allowed pupils to access revision websites, log into the school email system, or transfer electronic files between school and home.

The study, by researchers at Nottingham University, involved 331 pupils in schools in Cambridgeshire, West Berkshire and Nottingham.

'At the start of the study, even pupils were often surprised at the thought that mobile phones could be used for learning,' Dr Elizabeth Hartnell-Young will tell the annual conference of the British Educational Research Association in Edinburgh later today.

'After their hands-on experience, almost all pupils said they had enjoyed the project and felt more motivated.'

One teacher told researchers that students like mobiles and they know how to use them.

'Using this technology gives them more freedom to express themselves without needing to be constantly supervised,' the teacher said.

However, the report admits that some teachers think greater use of mobile phones in schools could prove problematic.

Increased temptation to steal phones belonging to the school was one worry. 'I thought, well, four of these smartphones are going to end up on eBay tomorrow,' one teacher said.

Other concerns related to cheating and taking inappropriate images or recordings of teachers.

Allowing pupils to access school emails via mobiles would also pose data security risks if passwords were shared, they said.

More than 90 per cent of secondary school pupils have their own mobile phones but their use is often forbidden on school premises.

Some schools ban them outright while others insist they must be kept switched off except in emergencies or outside lesson time.

However, the study found that despite the bans, some pupils were using their phones in class, including as cameras and to make calls to friends.

Dr Hartnell-Young said: 'While the eventual aim should be to lift blanket bans on phones, we do not recommend immediate, whole-school change. Instead, we believe that teachers, students and the wider community should work together to develop policies that will enable this powerful new learning tool to be used safely.'

Children should be allowed to use mobiles in class by Laura Clark

1 *Academics are calling on schools to rethink bans ....*

What does the word *academics* mean in this sentence?

_____

1

(1 mark)

2 From where are the academics who carried out the research?

_____

2

(1 mark)

3 **Find** and **copy two** tasks that, according to the report, the children used their smartphones for during the study.

1. _____

2. _____

3

(2 marks)

4 Write a headline for this text.

_____

4

(1 mark)

5 **Find** and **copy two** words or phrases that suggest that the ideas are opinions rather than facts.

1. _____

2. _____

5

(2 marks)

6 Using mobile phones in school has both positive and negative outcomes.

Give **one** positive outcome and **one** negative outcome, referring to the text in your answer.

Positive outcome:

_____

_____

Negative outcome:

_____

_____

6

(3 marks)

/ 10

Total for
this text

31

Snow shelters

These questions will help you practise:
★ explaining how information contributes to meaning
★ retrieving and recording information
★ explaining how language choices enhance meaning
★ explaining inferences.

Provided temperatures remain below 0°C (32°F), constructing snow shelters is relatively easy. These can range from a simple, hollowed-out heap of snow to an igloo, which can take a few hours to construct.

1 Cut blocks from dry, hard snow, using a snow saw or large knife. Each block should be about 1 m (3 ft) long, 40 cm (15 in) high, and 20 cm (8 in) deep.

2 Form a circle with blocks around the hole created where you cut the blocks. Cut the circle in a spiral from the top of the last block to the ground ahead of the first block. This will make it easy to construct a dome.

3 Build up the walls, overlapping the blocks and shaping them so that they lean inwards. Cut a hole under the wall for the **cold sink** and entrance. Put several blocks along one wall as a sleeping platform.

4 The last block must initially be larger than the hole. Place the block on top of the igloo, then, from inside, shape and wiggle it to slot exactly into the hole.

5 Hot air from your body and stove rises and is trapped inside the dome. Cold air falls into the sink and flows away to the outside. It is essential to cut ventilation holes in the walls with an ice axe.

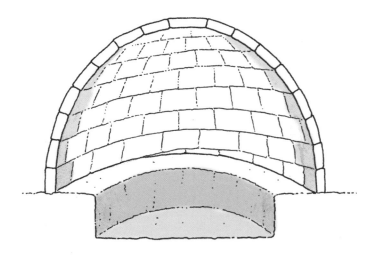

Warning

It is vital to make at least one air hole in the roof to avoid suffocation. The igloo will get very warm inside with heat from your body, even if it is cold and windy outside. Without ventilation, lethal carbon monoxide will build up.

The Commando Survival Manual
by Hugh McManners

Glossary
• **cold sink** low trench

1 a) What is the purpose of this text?

_____

1a
(1 mark)

b) Choose **two** features of the text to support your answer.

1. _____

2. _____

1b
(2 marks)

2 a) Look at the section headed: **Warning** and the paragraph for step 5.

Here the writer uses two different words which mean _important_.

Find and **copy both** words.

1. _____

2. _____

2a
(2 marks)

b) What is the effect of using these words?

_____

_____

2b
(1 mark)

3 **Brackets** are used four times in the text.

What is the purpose of the brackets?

_____

3
(1 mark)

4 Who do you think is the intended audience for this text?

Explain fully, referring to the text in your answer.

4
(3 marks)

_____

_____

_____

_____

_____

/ 10

Total for
this text

33

The travels of Marianne North

These questions will help you practise:
★ identifying and explaining how information is related
★ identifying and explaining how language choices enhance meaning
★ giving the meaning of words in context
★ making comparisons
★ retrieving and recording information
★ explaining inferences.

Brazil
October 1872

Such scenery! High trees draped with bougainvillea to the very tops, bushes of the same nearer the ground reminding one of the great rhododendrons in our own shrubberies in May at home, and of much the same colour, though occasionally paler and pinker. There were orange-flowered cassia trees (whose leaves fold close together at night like the sensitive plant) and scarlet erythrinas looking like gems among the masses of rich green; exquisite peeps of the river, winding below its woody banks or rushing among great stones and rocks, came upon us, and were gone again with tantalising rapidity.

India
1878

It was delightful after a long night and day in the dusty train to find myself again opposite Benares; and the weather had become perfect, neither too hot nor too cold. I hired a carriage for the week and went every morning to sketch on the river, where there was such a mass of picturesqueness that the attempt to paint and reproduce it almost drove me to despair. Sitting in a boat anchored by a rope or a stone, with a fidgety man holding an umbrella between me and the cloudless morning sun, is not a comfortable mode of painting.

Australia
1880

But it was always raining in this unexpected bit of the tropics, and I had no easy task to finish a picture there. Three times I packed up my things in disgust, and at last brought home my paper wetter with rain than with oil paint.... Another day I stopped to paint a gigantic fig tree standing alone, its huge buttresses covered with tangled creepers and parasites.

South Africa
January 1883

So I painted more flowers. A loranthus (tree parasite) was very interesting. When I touched the end of the bud, if ripe, it suddenly burst, and the petals sprang backwards, while the pistil in the middle, which was curved like the spring of a watch, was jerked out a yard or more. A tree called the wild pear (Dombeya rotundifolia) was just in full bloom, and very conspicuous in the landscape with its fine white flowers.

Abundant Beauty: The Adventurous Travels of Marianne North Introduction by Laura Ponsonby

1 Look at the section about Brazil.

a) **Find** and **copy one** word that is similar in meaning to 'perfect'.

_____

1a (1 mark)

b) Look at the section about India.
Find and **copy one** word that is similar in meaning to 'style' or 'type'.

_____

1b (1 mark)

2 a) The writer has used similes in this extract.
Find and **copy one** of the similes.

_____

2a (1 mark)

b) Explain the effect of using the simile.

_____
_____

2b (1 mark)

3 *A tree called the wild pear (Dombeya rotundifolia) was just in full bloom, and very conspicuous in the landscape with its fine white flowers.*

What does the word *conspicuous* mean in this sentence?

_____

3 (1 mark)

4 How did the weather in Australia compare to the weather in India?

_____

4 (1 mark)

5 According to the information in the text, in which country would you find trees with orange flowers?

_____

5 (1 mark)

6 What job do you think the writer has?
Refer fully to the text in your answer.

_____
_____
_____
_____
_____

6 (3 marks)

/ 10

Total for this text

35

Dumping waste in the sea

These questions will help you practise:
★ summarising main ideas
★ giving the meaning of words in context
★ retrieving and recording information
★ making inferences
★ identifying how information contributes to meaning
★ explaining inferences.

Five bags full of plastic for every foot of world's coast

…that's eight million tons being dumped into the sea each year

So much plastic is dumped into the sea each year that it would fill five carrier bags for every foot of coastline on the planet, scientists have warned.

Around eight million tons of plastic bottles, bags, toys and other plastic rubbish ends up in the world's oceans each year.

The 'staggering' total is much higher than previous estimates – and enough to leave an area around 25 times the size of Manchester ankle-deep in plastic waste.

Because of the difficulties in working out the exact amount, since much of it may have sunk, the scientists said the true figure could be as much as 12.7 million tons polluting the ocean each year.

Dr Jenna Jambeck, one of the researchers from the University of Georgia in the US, said, 'We are becoming overwhelmed by our waste.'

The team also warned that this 'ocean of plastic' can harm sea life.

Turtles can mistake plastic bags for jellyfish and eat them. The bags then block their stomachs which cause them to starve to death.

Sea birds also often mistake floating plastic for food; over 90 per cent of **fulmars** found dead around the North Sea have plastic in their stomachs. It is also feared that it could harm our health to eat fish that have consumed plastic.

The scientists reached their figures by analysing data on the amount of waste generated and how well it is disposed of in 192 coastal countries.

This included litter left on beaches as well as plastic from **fly-tipping** and badly-managed rubbish dumps.

Five bags full of plastic by Fiona MacRae

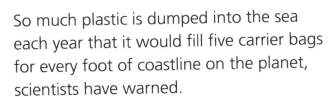

Glossary
- **fulmar** gull-sized grey and white seabird
- **fly-tipping** illegal dumping of waste

1 What is the main thing that the text is trying to tell you? Explain in **one** sentence.

_____

1
(1 mark)

2 _The 'staggering' total is much higher than previous estimates._ What does the word _staggering_ mean in this sentence?

_____

2
(1 mark)

3 What **two** things does the text say the researchers looked at to come up with their figures?

1. _____

2. _____

3
(2 marks)

4 Tick one box in each row to show whether each statement is a **fact** or an **opinion**.

	Fact	Opinion
The figure could be as much as 12.7 million tons each year.		
Millions of tons of plastic end up in the sea.		
Fulmars have been found dead.		
It could harm our health to eat fish.		
Much of the plastic may have sunk.		

4
(1 mark)

5 What is the purpose of this text? Tick **one**.

to explain and instruct ☐   to entertain and persuade ☐

to inform and persuade ☐   to explain and inform ☐

5
(1 mark)

6 Why do you think scientists might be concerned about the amount of plastic in the seas and oceans?

Explain fully and refer to the text in your answer.

_____
_____
_____
_____

6
(3 marks)

/ 9

Total for
this text

How to make a double helix

Almost all organisms, including human beings, have a 'genetic fingerprint', determined by their DNA. The DNA molecules hold information about an organism's inherited traits, and they can copy themselves by 'unzipping' down the middle and re-generating their missing half. Here, you can make a simplified model of a DNA molecule, showing all the components.

You will need
- inner tube of a kitchen roll • pen • wire
- modelling clay in two colours • toothpicks
- adhesive tape • scissors

1. Using the kitchen-roll tube as a template, curl the wire up around it in a spiral. Follow the seam on the tube to keep the coils evenly spaced. Make another identical spiral (helix).

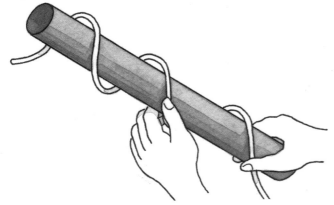

2. Mould the modelling clay into 12 balls in each colour. These balls represent the sugars and phosphates on the outside of the molecule. Thread them onto each helix, alternating the colours as you go. Make sure that both helixes start with the same colour. Wrap strips of adhesive tape around the wire above and below the balls to hold them in place.

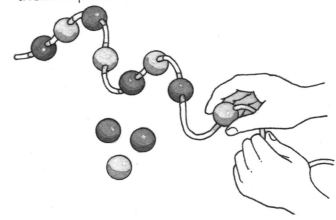

3. Cut the ends off the toothpicks, then colour half of each with the pen. These two-coloured sticks represent the pairs of chemical compounds (bases) that join the helixes together. Line up the wires so that they intertwine, then use the sticks to link each pair of clay balls in one colour. The sticks should run horizontally across the centre of the model.

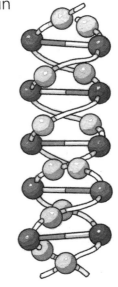

Making a double helix by Carol Vorderman

38

1 a) What is the purpose of this text?

_____

1a

b) Choose **two** features to support your answer.

1. _____

2. _____

1b (2 marks)

2 **Find** and **copy one** fact from the section beginning: _Almost all organisms ...._

_____

2 (1 mark)

3 Following the introduction, how is the text organised?

Tick **one**.

in no particular order ☐
in order of colours ☐
in chronological order ☐
in order of resources used ☐

3 (1 mark)

4 In step 1, the writer uses a word that means _guide_.

Find and **copy** the word.

_____

4 (1 mark)

5 a) **Find** and **copy three** command words.

_____

5a (1 mark)

b) Explain why commands are used in this text.

_____

_____

5b (1 mark)

/ 8

Total for this text 39

Jousting

These questions will help you practise:
★ identifying and explaining how information contributes to meaning as a whole
★ giving the meaning of words in context
★ explaining how language choices enhance meaning
★ identifying key details
★ explaining inferences
★ making comparisons.

Jousting and Tournaments

Jousting tournaments not only provided entertainment for the crowds but helped to sharpen up a knight's combat skills without the dangers associated with battle.

Main types of competition

There were two types, a 'joust a plaisance' and a 'pas d'armes'. The first of these events was a series of elimination contests that took place over several days until a single winner was found. In the second, a knight would send out a proclamation that he would take on all-comers at a certain place and time.

Special arenas

Contests were held in a special arena called 'the lists'. A long barrier, like a fence, ran down the centre of the lists and knights did battle across the barrier as they rode towards each other from opposite ends. Points were awarded for hitting an opponent's shield with the lance, breaking off a lance tip and unseating the rider from his horse. If both riders had been unseated, fighting could continue on foot using swords and shields.

Identification

Knights fighting in battle or taking part in a friendly jousting tournament could not be recognised because of the increasing amount of armour they were wearing, especially full-face helmets. So they took to wearing and carrying their own distinctive badges called coats of arms (heraldry). These were worn on the thin surcoats that covered armour but later were added to banners and flags, horse coverings, shields and the tabards (tunics) worn by their servants.

A coat of seven colours

Coats of arms were made up of a combination of *tinctures* (colours), *ordinaires* (layout designs) and *symbols* (shapes, creatures, flowers and objects). The only colours allowed were the two metals, gold (*or*) and silver (*argent*) plus green (*vert*), blue (*azure*), black (*sable*), red (*gules*) and purple (*pupure*).

> ### Did you know?
>
> During the Crusades, more knights died from disease than from wounds received in battle.
>
> Knights in tournaments often wore a coloured scarf or a ribbon to show they were dedicating their performance to the lady who had given it to them.

Aquila magazine

1 a) What is the purpose of this text?

_____

b) Choose **two** features of the text to support your answer.

1. _____

2. _____

2 _In the second, a knight would send out a proclamation…_
What does the word _proclamation_ mean in this sentence?

_____

3 Many jousting terms are written in French.
How does the writer help the reader to understand these terms?
Give **two** ways and refer to the text in your answer.

_____
_____
_____

4 Knights had great strength and determination.
Give **one** detail to support this idea.

_____

5 Who do you think is the intended audience for this text?
Refer to the text in your answer.

_____
_____

6 How does the information in the **_Did you know?_** box compare
with the idea that knights were strong?

_____
_____
_____
_____
_____

The life of Adrian Henri

These questions will help you practise:
* ★ identifying key details
* ★ identifying how language choices enhance meaning
* ★ identifying how narrative content is related
* ★ explaining how narrative content contributes to meaning as a whole
* ★ making and explaining inferences.

Carrying my gas mask to school every day
buying saving stamps
Remembering my National Registration Number
ZMGM/136/3 (see I can still remember it)
avoiding Careless Talk
Digging for Victory
looking for German spies everywhere
Oh yes, I did my bit for my country that long dark winter,
me and Winston and one or two others,
wearing my tin hat whenever possible
singing 'Hang out the washing on the Siegfried Line'
aircraft-recognition charts pinned to my bedroom wall
the smell of paint on toy soldiers
doing paintings of Spitfires and Hurricanes, Lancasters
and Halifaxes
always with a Heinkel or a Messerschmitt plunging
helplessly into the sea in the background
pink light in the sky from Liverpool burning 50 miles away
the thunder of daylight flying fortresses high overhead
shaking the elderberry tree
bright barrage-balloons flying over the docks
morning curve of the bay seen from the park on the hill
after coming out of the air-raid shelter
listening for the all clear siren
listening to Vera Lynn, Dorothy Lamour, Allen Jones
and The Andrew Sisters
clutching my father's hand tripping over the unfamiliar kerb
I walk over every day
in the black-out.

Autobiography by Adrian Henri

1 In this text, the writer is remembering his childhood.

Give **two** details from his memory that are given in the text.

1. _____

2. _____

2 *the thunder of daylight flying fortresses high overhead*

What might *daylight flying fortresses* be?

_____

3 The writer uses senses such as sight in the poem.

Which other senses does the writer use?

Give evidence from the text to support your answer.

_____

_____

4 The writer uses several examples of present tense verbs such as *shaking, remembering, singing, wearing.*

What is the purpose of using these verbs?

_____

5 What impression does the text give you about the writer's safety during the war?

Refer to the text in your answer.

_____
_____
_____
_____
_____

6 What do you think the writer is trying to explain by saying 'tripping over the unfamiliar kerb I walk over every day'?

_____

Pleasant sounds

These questions will help you practise:
★ retrieving and recording information
★ identifying and explaining how language choices enhance meaning
★ summarising main ideas.

The rustling of leaves under the feet in woods and
  under hedges;

The crumping of **cat-ice** and snow down wood-rides
  narrow lanes, and every street causeway;

Rustling through a wood or rather rushing, while the
  wind **halloos** in the oak-top like thunder;

The rustle of birds' wings startled from their nests or
  flying unseen into the bushes;

The whizzing of larger birds overhead in a wood,
  such as crows, **puddocks**, buzzards;

The trample of robins and woodlarks on the brown
  leaves, and the patter of squirrels on the green
  moss;

The fall of an acorn on the ground, the pattering of
  nuts on the hazel branches as they fall from
  ripeness;

The flirt of the groundlark's wing from the **stubbles** –
  how sweet such pictures on dewy mornings,
  when the dew flashes from its brown feathers!

John Clare

Glossary

- **cat-ice** thin ice with no water beneath
- **halloos** greetings
- **puddocks** large bird
- **stubbles** stalks of hay on a field after harvesting

1 What do the robins and woodlark trample on in the poem?

_____

1 (1 mark)

2 a) The writer has used onomatopoeia in the poem.

Find and **copy one** example.

_____

2a (1 mark)

b) How is this effective in the poem?

_____

_____

2b (1 mark)

3 **Find** and **copy** an example of alliteration in the poem.

_____

3 (1 mark)

4 a) **Find** and **copy** the simile in the poem.

_____

4a (1 mark)

b) Explain the effect of the simile.

_____

_____

4b (1 mark)

5 Write a title for this poem.

Explain why you have chosen this title, referring to the text in your answer.

_____

_____

_____

_____

_____

5 (3 marks)

The magic of the brain

Such a sight I saw:
An eight-sided kite surging up into a cloud
Its eight tails streaming out as if they were one.
It lifted my heart as starlight lifts the head
Such a sight I saw.

And such a sound I heard:
One bird through dim winter light as the day was closing
Poured out a song suddenly from an empty tree.
It cleared my head as water refreshes the skin
Such a sound I heard.

Such a smell I smelled:
A mixture of roses and coffee, of green leaf and warmth.
It took me to gardens and summer and cities abroad,
Memories of meetings as if my past friends were here
Such a smell I smelled.

Such a soft fur I felt:
It wrapped me around, soothing my winter-cracked skin,
Not gritty or stringy or sweaty but silkily warm
As my animal slept on my lap, and we both breathed content
Such soft fur I felt.

Such food I tasted:
Smooth-on-tongue soup, and juicy crackling of meat,
Greens like fresh fields, sweet-on-your-palate peas,
Jellies and puddings and fragrance of fruit they are made from
Such good food I tasted.

Such a world comes in:
Far world of the sky to breathe in through your nose
Near world you feel underfoot as you walk on the land.
Through your eyes and your ears and your mouth and your brilliant brain
Such a world comes in.

Jenny Joseph

1 What is the writer using to experience the world?

_____

1 (1 mark)

2 How does the writer keep warm in winter?

_____

2 (1 mark)

3 Look at the verse beginning: _Such food I tasted…._

Explain how you know the writer is using another sense in this verse.

Refer to the poem in your answer.

_____

_____

3 (1 mark)

4 What is the purpose of using a colon at the end of the first line of each verse?

_____

_____

4 (1 mark)

5 The poem contains details of how the writer felt.

Find and **copy** a phrase to support this idea.

_____

5 (1 mark)

6 Explain the effect of repeating the first and last line of every verse.

_____

_____

6 (1 mark)

7 What is the main idea in the last verse of the poem?

_____

_____

7 (1 mark)

/7

Total for this text

The harvest

These questions will help you practise:
* ★ summarising main ideas
* ★ identifying and explaining how language choices enhance meaning
* ★ identifying how narrative content contributes to meaning as a whole
* ★ giving the meaning of words in context
* ★ making comparisons.

Late August, given heavy rain and sun

For a full week, the blackberries would ripen.

At first, just one, a glossy purple **clot**

Among others, red, green, hard as a knot.

You ate that first one and its flesh was sweet

Like thickened wine: summer's blood was in it

Leaving stains upon the tongue and lust for

Picking. Then red ones inked up and that hunger

Sent us out with milk-cans, pea-tins, jam-pots

Where briars scratched and wet grass bleached our boots.

Round hayfields, cornfields and potato-drills

We trekked and picked until the cans were full,

Until the tinkling bottom had been covered

With green ones, and on top big dark blobs burned

Like a plate of eyes. Our hands were peppered

With thorn pricks, our palms sticky as Bluebeard's.

We hoarded the fresh berries in the **byre**.

But when the bath was filled we found a fur,

A rat-grey fungus, **glutting** on our cache.

The juice was stinking too. Once off the bush

The fruit fermented, the sweet flesh would turn sour.

I always felt like crying. It wasn't fair

That all the lovely canfuls smelt of rot.

Each year I hoped they'd keep, knew they would not.

Seamus Heaney

Glossary
* **clot** mass or lump
* **byre** cowshed
* **glutting** eating up greedily

1 Write a suitable alternative title for this poem.

_____

2 a) In the first verse, what does the writer compare the flesh of the blackberries to?

_____

b) Explain how this is effective.

_____

_____

3 This poem is about a memory from the writer's childhood.

Give **two** features to support this.

1. _____

2. _____

4 _A rat-grey fungus, glutting on our cache._

What does the word _cache_ mean in this sentence?

_____

5 Explain how the writer builds a picture of the setting.

Refer fully to the text in your answer.

_____

_____

_____

_____

_____

_____

6 How is the quality of the blackberries different at the start of the poem compared to the end of the poem?

_____

_____

_____

Stop all the clocks

These questions will help you practise:
★ making inferences
★ giving the meaning of words in context
★ identifying and explaining how narrative content contributes to meaning as a whole
★ making comparisons
★ identifying how language choices enhance meaning
★ explaining inferences.

Stop all the clocks, cut off the telephone,
Prevent the dog from barking with a juicy bone,
Silence the pianos and with muffled drum
Bring out the coffin, let the mourners come.

Let aeroplanes circle moaning overhead
Scribbling on the sky the message He is Dead,
Put crepe bows round the white necks of the public doves,
Let the traffic policemen wear black cotton gloves.

He was my North, my South, my East and West,
My working week and my Sunday rest,
My noon, my midnight, my talk, my song;
I thought that love would last for ever: I was wrong.

The stars are not wanted now: put out every one;
Pack up the moon and dismantle the sun,
Pour away the ocean and sweep up the wood.
For nothing now can ever come to any good.

Funeral Blues by W.H. Auden

1 This poem was written in response to what event?

_____

2 *… let the mourners come.*

What does the word *mourners* mean in this sentence?

_____

3 a) **Find** and **copy two** command verbs from the first verse.

1. _____

2. _____

b) Explain the effect of using these commands.

_____

4 How are the things the writer describes in the first verse **different** to those in the fourth verse?

_____

_____

5 **Find** and **copy** an example of metaphor in the poem.

_____

6 Some of the writer's demands to stop things happening may be possible, whilst others may be impossible.

Explain what the possibilities are, referring to the text in your answer.

_____

_____

_____

_____

_____

The Pied Piper of Hamelin

These questions will help you practise:
★ understanding words in context
★ identifying and explaining how narrative content contributes to meaning as a whole
★ identifying and explaining how language choices enhance meaning
★ explaining the meaning of words in context.

'Come in!' – the Mayor cried, looking bigger:
And in did come the strangest figure!
His queer long coat from heel to head
Was half of yellow and half of red
And he himself was tall and thin,
With sharp blue eyes, each like a pin,
And light loose hair, yet **swarthy** skin,
No tuft on cheek nor beard on chin,
But lips where smiles went out and in –
There was no guessing his **kith and kin**!
And nobody could enough admire
The tall man and his **quaint attire**.
Quoth one: 'It's as if my great-grandsire,
Starting up at the Trump of Doom's tone,
Had walked this way from his painted tombstone!'

Into the street the Piper stept,
Smiling first a little smile,
As if he knew what magic slept
In his quiet pipe the while;
Then, like a musical **adept**,
To blow the pipe his lips he wrinkled,
And green and blue his sharp eyes twinkled,
Like a candle-flame where salt is sprinkled;
And **ere** three shrill notes the pipe uttered,
You heard as if an army muttered;
And the muttering grew to a grumbling;
And the grumbling grew to a mighty rumbling;
And out of the houses the rats came tumbling.
Great rats, small rats, lean rats, brawny rats,
Brown rats, black rats, gray rats, tawny rats,
Grave old plodders, gay young friskers,
Fathers, mothers, uncles, cousins,
Cocking tails and pricking whiskers,
Families by tens and dozens,
Brothers, sisters, husbands, wives –
Followed the Piper for their lives.

Robert Browning

Glossary
- **swarthy** dark
- **kith and kin** family
- **quaint** old-fashioned
- **attire** clothing
- **adept** skilled
- **ere** before

1 **Find** and **copy** the word that tells you the Piper was unusual.

_____

2 Look at the first verse. What is the purpose of using so many **adjectives**?
Give **two** reasons.

1. _____

2. _____

3 Some of the language used in this poem is no longer used today.
Give **two** examples.

1. _____

2. _____

4 _And ere three shrill notes the pipe uttered._
Explain why the word _shrill_ is an appropriate word to describe the notes of the pipe.

_____

_____

5 The writer compares the Piper's eyes to a candle flame.
Explain the effect of doing this.

_____

_____

6 a) Towards the end of the second verse, the number of words in each line decreases. This is so the reader...

Tick **one**.

reads slowly. ☐

reads at the same pace. ☐

reads quickly. ☐

gradually slows down. ☐

b) Explain the image the writer is trying to create by doing this.

_____

_____

Night mail

These questions will help you practise:
* ★ summarising main ideas
* ★ identifying and explaining how language choices enhance meaning
* ★ identifying and explaining how narrative content is related and contributes to meaning as a whole
* ★ making comparisons.

This is the night mail crossing the border,
Bringing the cheque and the postal order,
Letters for the rich, letters for the poor,
The shop at the corner and the girl next door.
Pulling up **Beattock**, a steady climb –
The gradient's against her, but she's on time.

Past cotton grass and moorland boulder
Shovelling white steam over her shoulder,
Snorting noisily as she passes
Silent miles of wind-bent grasses.
Birds turn their heads as she approaches,
Stare from the bushes at her blank-faced
    coaches.
Sheep dogs cannot turn her course,
They slumber on with paws across.
In the farm she passes no one wakes,
But the jug in the bedroom gently shakes.
Dawn freshens, the climb is done.
Down towards Glasgow she descends
Towards the steam tugs yelping down the
    glade of cranes,
Towards the fields of apparatus, the furnaces
Set on the dark plain like gigantic chessmen.
All Scotland waits for her:
In the dark glens, beside the pale-green lochs
Men long for news.
Letters of thanks, letters from banks,
Letters of joy from the girl and the boy,

Receipted bills and invitations
To inspect new stock or visit relations,
And applications for situations
And timid lovers' declarations
And gossip, gossip from all the nations,
News circumstantial, news financial,
Letters with holiday snaps to enlarge in,
Letters with faces scrawled in the margin,
Letters from uncles, cousins and aunts,
Letters to Scotland from the South of France,
Letters of condolence to Highlands and
    Lowlands
Notes from overseas to Hebrides
Written on paper of every hue,
The pink, the violet, the white and the blue,
The chatty, the catty, the boring, adoring,
The cold and official and the heart's
    outpouring,
Clever, stupid, short and long,
The typed and the printed and the spelt all
    wrong.

W.H. Auden

Glossary

* **Beattock** a village in Scotland that is the highest point on this railway line

1 What is the main idea in the poem?
Explain in **one** sentence.

_____

1
(1 mark)

2 **Find** and **copy** an example of alliteration in the poem.

_____

_____

_____

2
(1 mark)

3 The word _letters_ is repeated eight times in the section beginning:
Letters of thanks....

What is the effect of repeating this word?

_____

_____

3
(1 mark)

4 a) The rhythm and the pace of the poem change in each section.

What do you notice about the pace in the section beginning:
Letters of thanks, letters from banks?

_____

4a
(1 mark)

b) Explain the effect of this change in pace.

_____

_____

_____

4b
(3 marks)

5 How is the setting in the section beginning _Past cotton grass ..._
different to the setting in the section beginning _Dawn freshens,
the climb is done...?_

Refer to the text in your answer.

_____

_____

_____

_____

_____

5
(3 marks)

/ 10

Total for
this text